The Words that Make Life Work

Daily Self-Talk Messages from the Dean of Positive Self-Talk

Shad Helmstetter, Ph.D., is the author of 19 books in the field of self-talk and personal growth, including *What to Say When You Talk to Your Self* and *The Power of Neuroplasticity*. His books are published in more than 70 countries worldwide. Shad has appeared on over 1200 radio and television programs, including repeat appearances on Oprah Winfrey, ABC, CBS, NBC, and CNN News.

You are invited to join Self-Talk+Plus™

If you would like to join an online community of positive self-talkers—people like you who are working to make their lives better—you are invited to join Self-Talk+Plus™. This is the inspiring online community where members stream self-talk to their smartphones, get to know each other, join in online activities, receive help from experienced life coaches, and share ideas that help them reach their goals. To visit this amazing online community go to **selftalkplus.com**.

 Listen to Certified Self-Talk Programs™ on your tablet or smartphone today at selftalkplus.com.

365 Days of
Positive Self-Talk
for
Weight-Loss

by Shad Helmstetter, Ph.D.

An Inspirational Guide
with Positive Self-Talk Messages
for Every Day of the Year

Includes 'Self-Talk Tips' for Putting Positive
Self-Talk to Work in Your Life

Also by Shad Helmstetter, Ph.D.

The Power of Neuroplasticity
365 Days of Positive Self-Talk
365 Days of Positive Self-Talk for Finding Your Purpose
365 Days of Positive Self-Talk for Recovery
365 Days of Positive Self-Talk for Network Marketing
365 Days of Positive Self-Talk for Stress
365 Days of Positive Self-Talk for Selling
365 Days of Positive Self-Talk for Self-Esteem
What to Say When You Talk to Your Self

365 Days of Positive Self-Talk
for Weight-Loss

Published by Park Avenue Press
362 Gulf Breeze Pkwy., #104
Gulf Breeze, FL 32561
Copyright 2016 by Shad Helmstetter, Ph.D. / All rights reserved

Helmstetter, Shad
    365 Days of Positive Self-Talk for Weight-Loss

ISBN 978-0-9727821-6-6 *Printed format*
ISBN 978-0-9727821-7-3 *Digital format*

www.selftalkplus.com

Before You Begin . . .

Some starting words to help you
get the most from reading this book,
and *three secrets you need to know.*

Welcome to the 365 Days of Positive Self-Talk series. This series of books is designed to give you daily self-talk in a variety of important interest areas, including individual books on self-talk for recovery, weight-loss, network marketing, selling, success in school, dealing with stress, and others to come.

Self-Talk for Weight-Loss

This book contains self-talk that is specifically designed to motivate and inspire anyone who wants to lose weight, keep it off, and focus on health and wellness. It also includes the important self-talk 'basics'—self-talk that is foundational to key areas of life that influence weight and fitness—including your self-esteem, goals, attitude, and determination to succeed.

All of your self-talk is important. The words you say, especially the words you say when you talk to your*self*, not only change your day, they change your life.

This book is based on the amazing scientific discovery that no matter what age you are, your brain continues to change, and that it is *always* changing. Because of your brain's neuroplasticity, your brain is designed to continually rewire itself. And it rewires itself based on the input it gets. That's why your self-talk is incredibly important.

Secret #1: The thoughts you think and the words you say *physically* and *chemically* change your brain. Your self-talk literally wires your brain to succeed or fail.

Day after day, word by word, your self-talk is wiring programs into your brain. And the picture of you that you wire in most is what you get back out most. *It is your self-talk that creates the foundation for your success or failure in life.*

Right now, even as you're reading this, you're wiring and changing your brain.

Your self-talk is the commander of your ship, the director of your life. It is the brain's guiding hand that leads you in the right direction—or in the wrong direction. Your self-talk is the messenger that tells you which path you should follow, what to think and what to do next.

Every thought you think wires your brain to be happy or sad, positive or negative, in a good mood or a bad mood, open to new ideas or closed to them, believing in yourself or not believing in yourself, looking for alternatives or accepting defeat. In fact, everything about you is, at this moment, being influenced or controlled by your self-talk.

What Is Self-Talk and Why Is It So Important?

Self-talk is the direction you give to your brain that tells it how to run your life. Self-talk is everything you say when you talk to yourself. It is your conscious thoughts, and your unconscious thoughts, the thoughts you don't even know you're thinking. It is what you say out loud or what you say silently to yourself. And in its most important form, your self-talk is everything you say or think about *you*—how you feel about yourself—and what you think and what you believe about anything and everything.

Most of us recognize that when we were growing up, we got programmed—and we end up *becoming* those programs and living them out. The remarkable thing, and a great blessing about self-talk, is that you can change that programming. And when you change your programs, you change your life. That's what the *right* self-talk will do for you.

Secret #2: It's been estimated that as much as 77% or more of all of the programs each of us has right now are negative, false, counter-productive, or working against us.

Since it will always be up to each of us to get rid of the negative programs we have, and replace them with the positive kind, any tool that will help us change them can be a blessing. And self-talk is the best tool for changing our programs we have ever found.

In this book you'll find 365 daily self-talk scripts of the right kind of self-talk—the kind of self-talk we should have been getting in the first place. These self-talk scripts are the result of more than 35 years of studying self-talk and how it works, and writing and recording self-talk scripts in dozens of subject areas.

I first began writing self-talk scripts in the late 1970s. At that time, I was studying self-talk and its effects on personal success, and I was writing the first scripts for recording self-talk audio programs for people to listen to. We had learned that with repeated listening, people could permanently wire positive new messages into their brains, just by playing the recorded self-talk in the background.

At the time, the role that self-talk played in people's lives wasn't yet generally understood. Few people realized that their own self-talk, unconsciously repeated throughout each day, was actually programming their brain, and often in the wrong way.

My studies in this field led to the writing of 19 books on the subject of self-talk and personal growth. My first book, *What to Say When You Talk to Your Self,* introduced the subject of self-talk as we know it today. That book is now published in more than 70 countries, and its popularity shows how mainstream the concept of positive self-talk has become.

One of my recent books, *The Power of Neuroplasticity,* gives the latest updates on this amazing subject, and presents the science behind positive self-talk. It shows clearly that when it comes to its ability to change our lives, self-talk is based on solid science.

Clear, Positive Programs

In *365 Days of Positive Self-Talk for Weight-Loss,* you'll find daily self-talk messages for reprogramming your brain in a clear, positive way.

The self-talk messages have the power to become much more than a few words you read each day. Reading them, rereading them, and wiring them into your brain could do more than just uplift your year—it could uplift your life.

Reading the self-talk messages one day at a time will give you not only daily inspiration, but also a chance to make each day a better day. However, if you're looking for extra guidance or inspiration at any time, turn to any page to see what you find. If you're looking for an uplift, or need to get back on track, you're sure to find that the self-talk you need is just a few pages away.

If you want to get the greatest benefit from this book, read each day's self-talk message as you start your day, and read that same message again just before you go to sleep that night.

There's a reason for doing this that has to do with the way the brain gets programmed. Every time you send a message to your brain, your brain *physically, chemically,* records it temporarily. The more positive messages your brain gets, the more positive directions it will record—and in time, with enough repetition, your brain will go beyond recording them temporarily; it will "wire them in," by creating new neural pathways, and act on them.

Each time you read the positive self-talk phrases in this book, you're sending more healthy messages to your brain. The more you repeat these messages, the stronger and more permanent they become. So you're literally rewiring your own brain with healthy, positive thoughts and messages.

Is Positive Self-Talk Telling You the Truth?

When you first read or listen to positive self-talk, because it's positive and stated in the *present* tense, you might think, *"But that's not me,"* or *"That's not true about me."* That's because some self-talk can sound too good to be true. So is it?

The answer is that positive self-talk paints a new picture of how you're *choosing* to become. It may not sound like you or your life the first time you read it, but it defines the new choices you're making to *become* that way. It may not be you at the moment, but it's a picture of you that you're choosing to create.

The brain listens best to directions that are specific and detailed. The better your brain can see it, the better it can help you create it. That's why self-talk is worded in the *present tense*; to give your brain the clearest, completed picture possible of what you want to accomplish. The clearer the picture you give to your brain of who you want to become, and how you want your life to be, the better your brain will physically 'wire it in' and help you get it.

When you see an artist's illustration of the fabulous new home you're going to build, you don't look at the picture of your home and say, *"This isn't true,"* or *"This isn't real,"* just because your dream home isn't built yet. You look at the illustration of that beautiful new home and see yourself living in it! It may not be a touchable reality when you first imagine it, but it is a future reality in the process of becoming real.

That's what positive self-talk is: *it's a picture of you as you choose to become*—the picture of you you're telling your brain to create. The right self-talk is telling you the truth of who you *really* are, and what you choose to do now to bring the real you to life.

The Most Important Key to 'Success' is *Repetition, Repetition, Repetition*

Secret #3: What you repeat frequently, wires the brain. That's so important, it bears repeating: Repetition wires the brain. Because what you experience most, you 'wire in' most, the most important key to success is repetition.

Repetition is the key to wiring or rewiring your brain in the right way because of the way neural networks are formed in the brain. Neural pathways in the brain are formed by repeatedly sending electrical and chemical messages (your thoughts) over the same route—over and over again—like building a highway with layer after layer of concrete or asphalt.

In your brain, each time you travel over the same route—each time your brain receives a repeat of the same message—the pathway becomes stronger and stronger, until, with enough repeated passes, you've created a new 'highway of thought' in your brain.

When similar highways connect, "programs" are formed. These programs—inter-connected mental super highways—become our *beliefs*, our *attitudes*, and our *opinions* about everything. And we create all of them through repetition. Everything we believe, about anything, actually comes to us through repetition. Everything you believe about *yourself* also comes to you through repetition.

Now, when we want to rewire our brains with better programs, we use the same process. But this time we're repeating better messages—positive self-talk—and building new, more positive, neural networks in the brain.

A message that isn't repeated, only gives your brain a passing thought; it doesn't get wired in permanently. But the exact same message repeated often enough, creates a new neural pathway, and it becomes a 'permanent' part of who you are.

Highlight and Reread Your Favorite Self-Talk

When you find a daily self-talk message that you especially like, or one that speaks to you with special meaning, be sure to mark it so you can easily find it and come back to it.

Since the more often you repeat any self-talk message, the more you'll begin to wire it into your brain, it's a good idea to go back to those messages you'd like to make a permanent part of your positive programs, and read and reread them again.

People often learn to recite lines of their favorite poetry by reading them often. Some of the self-talk you'll find here is poetry for a positive mind, and you can learn and remember it by rereading it frequently.

Also, mark any messages you feel could help you at a later time, should you ever need them. Self-talk messages can offer encouragement, a helping hand, and can uplift your spirit when you need it most.

Reading Self-Talk Out Loud

You'll also benefit from reading the self-talk scripts out loud. When you read aloud you're engaging more senses and increasing your brain activity. When you're reading self-talk out loud and focusing on the message you're reading, you'll increase retention. Reading self-talk in this way isn't required to get the benefit of practicing self-talk, but it will help.

If you find reading aloud is not convenient—you may want privacy when you're reading out loud—or if you find it difficult to add to your schedule each day, just read the self-talk in a normal way, silently, to yourself. The most important thing is to read it, and make it as convenient as possible, so you'll have no reason not to stay with it.

Listening to Self-Talk

Along with reading self-talk each day, you may also want to add listening to self-talk to your daily schedule.

By itself, reading self-talk helps you see each day in a healthy way, and reading even one passage each morning and at night is a habit you should create. When you also listen to self-talk each day, it will help you rewire your brain in a stronger way, and it will do it faster.

Positive self-talk was first written and recorded to be listened to. (The first professionally recorded self-talk programs were introduced in 1981.) The idea proved to be so helpful that many thousands of people now listen to 10- to 20-minute self-talk sessions every day on their smartphones or other listening devices.

Recorded self-talk is different from the self-talk you find in this book. The recorded form of self-talk goes into greater detail; it is more in-depth in specific subject areas that are important to you personally, that you want to work on. In recorded self-talk, each self-talk phrase is also repeated three times, each time with different word emphasis and intonations that increase the strength of the message, and help the brain wire it in faster and stronger.

Recordings of subjects like self-talk for weight-loss, personal relationships, health and fitness, job and career, finances, self-esteem, etc., and even special self-talk for kids and young people, give the listener in-depth self-talk programs that are designed to be listened to each day.

When self-talk is listened to frequently—usually each day for two or three weeks on each subject area you want to work on—the daily repetition of the self-talk causes the brain to rewire itself naturally, and with the right programs. The more often your brain hears those same messages repeated, the stronger and faster they are wired in.

You can listen to all of the recorded self-talk programs that are certified by the Self-Talk Institute at selftalkplus.com.

"Self-Talk+Plus™"

While you're practicing self-talk each day, and you find that the idea of positive self-talk makes sense to you, if you'd like to have more help and support making self-talk a part of your life, and if you'd like to get to know other people who feel the same way, you are invited to join a wonderful community of positive self-talkers at Self-Talk+Plus.

Self-Talk+Plus is an online membership community that was created to bring self-talkers together, give people additional motivation and help, update my readers on the latest news and developments, and stream recorded self-talk audio programs so you can listen to any self-talk you choose at any time, like listening to your favorite online music. You're invited to join us at selftalkplus.com.

"Self-Talk Tips"

Throughout this book you'll also find useful *"Self-Talk Tips"*—helpful ideas and discoveries that will show you how positive self-talk works, where it comes from and what it can do for you.

Instead of waiting to read each *Self-Talk Tip* until you arrive at its place in the book, you may want to skip ahead and read through more of the tips, just as though you're reading a separate "how to" companion book of tips to help you get the most from the daily self-talk messages.

The importance of repetition in creating positive neural pathways in the brain is so important, that some of the key points will be expressed, in different ways, more than once. If you find a key concept idea that is repeated, that's not an accident. That's how the brain gets it, holds it, and, with enough repetition, wires it in.

Enjoy Each Day, and Enjoy the Journey

I hope you'll find the self-talk both uplifting and helpful. And I hope that among the many self-talk messages in these pages, you'll find some of the answers in your quest for the incredible person you were designed to be. To get started, all you have to do is choose a date, go to that page, and let the journey begin.

January 1

"Of everything I look forward to this year, I especially look forward to making each new day a health and fitness day. Throughout the year I'm following my plan, staying with it, and reaching my goal."

January 2

"Now is a perfect time to get myself in shape. I choose to be healthy and fit, so I eat right, I get the exercise I need, and I make sure I get the right amount of rest and relaxation. And I make sure I give my mind a healthy diet of self-talk that builds my attitude, shows me at my best, and motivates me to reach my goals."

January 3

"Today I choose to be at my best and make my day work in every positive way. Today I'm completely in touch with who I am, what I want, and where I'm going. Today is a day I move my life forward. I know what I want to accomplish, I take action, I go for it, and I get it done!"

January 4

"Almost any problem I think I face right now, is not really a problem at all. Because I choose to deal with it, in not too long, it will be gone; in time, it will be forgotten. The moment I realize that, my life gets better."

January 5

"Reaching my goal to be fit and healthy, and being the 'me' that I really want to be is easy for me now. My attitude, my actions, and every word of my self-talk are helping me every day."

January 6

"My weight and fitness goals are important to me. I believe in doing everything I need to do to improve myself and make my life better. I eat right, exercise, stay with it and reach my goals."

Self-Talk Tip #1
In Weight-Loss, the Strongest Program Wins

In the brain, the programs that are the strongest outweigh the other programs that aren't as strong.

That means that if your programs to eat that extra piece of chocolate cake are stronger than your programs to not eat it, the stronger program will win—and you'll eat the cake. But the opposite also is true.

If you have wired in to your brain, super strong, super healthy programs that help you make better, healthier decisions, then *those* programs will win, and you'll make the better choice.

The rule is, in the brain, the strongest programs always win. So the programs you wire in now, with positive self-talk—if you practice them so they grow into super programs—will literally help you overcome the temptation to fall off your diet, or deal with any problem you're working on.

Diet, income, work, relationships, family matters, self-esteem—whatever you're working on—the strongest programs you have wired into your brain will be the programs that win.

January 7

"If I want to make something of myself, it's up to me. It's not other people's doubts that count; it's my belief in me. It's not the challenges I face each day; it's my determination to overcome them. It's not the lack of opportunities in front of me; it's my willingness to find them. My success is not up to the world around me, or up to someone else; my success is up to me."

January 8

"I choose to surround myself with success. I spend time with positive people who believe in me. I read books that enlighten me. I fill my life with messages that inspire me. I write, read, and reread goals that motivate me. I know I will become the person who is a reflection of the world that I allow to surround me most. And I choose to surround myself with success."

January 9

"When I choose the right, healthy weight for me, I know what I want, and I know how I want to be. And I know that the self-talk I practice every day will help take me there."

January 10

"I choose, forever, to remove the fear that I might not 'measure up' to someone else. I never measure my life by the expectations of others. I live my life based on my own positive expectations to live each day in the very best way. And every day, I measure up to me."

January 11

"With my health and fitness, as in all things that I do, I take care of the things that matter most. I never ignore what needs my attention. Instead of worrying about the unimportant details of life, I focus my attention on the things that count."

January 12

"I am ready and willing to pay the positive price to achieve my health and fitness goals. And I know that the real price is my willingness and my determination to change."

Self-Talk Tip #2
The 'Healthy You' That Lives Within

Behavioral researchers have long known that if you can imagine your success at anything clearly enough, your chances of actually creating that success improve. With weight-loss, that's especially important because how you *see* yourself most is likely who you will become.

That's why you should practice, every day, seeing yourself looking like you would most like to be. When you see yourself in your mind, be realistic, but always practice seeing yourself as your healthiest self—weighing exactly what you want to weigh, and looking great. You don't have to be there yet, but the self-picture you focus on today is going to help you create that picture, for real, in your future.

You have a very healthy you that lives within you. It's built into your DNA. It weighs the right weight, it always wants you to live right, eat right, and always be as healthy as you can possibly be. When you practice seeing *that* picture of you in your mind every day, that's the you you'll bring to life. And stay with it. What you imagine most today is who you become most tomorrow.

January 13

"There is no problem I cannot conquer, there is no challenge I cannot overcome. I have been given every talent and ability I need to succeed in anything I choose to achieve. If I want to do it, I can do it. And if I want to make it happen in my life, making it happen is up to me."

January 14

"I know that the real secret to my success in reaching and maintaining the weight I want gets down to my undying persistence, and my absolute determination to reach my goal. So I start, I stay with it, and I keep going. And because I will not give up, I reach my goal.

January 15

"Each day is another chance for me to restart my life—with promise, opportunity, and unlimited potential. No matter where I've been until now, I have the most important part of my life in front of me, and I'm just now getting started."

January 16

"I really enjoy making this healthy new change in my life. Working at reaching my weight and fitness goals is exciting, energizing, satisfying, and fulfilling in so many ways."

January 17

"I have spirit, I have faith, and I am blessed in so many ways! I am filled with life, full of hope, and determined to live up to my greatest potential."

January 18

"I know I can reach and maintain any weight goal I set for myself. I have the reason. I have the plan. I have the right attitude. And I have the determination to stay with it and reach my goal."

Self-Talk Tip #3
More Than a Few Good Words

Positive self-talk is more than just saying a few kind words to yourself now and then. It's much more than that.

Positive self-talk is the best way we've ever found to rewire our brains with the right programs. Along with that, it's a way of getting rid of the wrong programs—the ones that continually work against us.

Practicing positive self-talk is also a way of living; it's an attitude you adopt that becomes an important part of who you are. It's a way of taking control of your life, who you are, how you think, the goals you set and how successful you are at reaching them.

As one definition puts it, self-talk is: "positive, self-directed, neuron patterning, personal mind-brain programming."

We just call it self-talk.

January 19

"Today I choose to be strong, confident, sure of myself, and unafraid. I know what I'm going for. I have an incredible attitude. I know I can do it, get past the negatives, focus everything I do on the most positive outcome, and do it."

January 20

"If I had one day, one time, one moment, to live up to my best, take action, get things done, move forward and excel, I would do it. And as soon as I think the thought, I know the truth: Today is the day, this is the time, and right now is the moment."

January 21

"Each new day is a chance for me to live up to my dreams. What I want to do, I can do. What I want to achieve, I can achieve. And who I want to become, I can become. I choose to dream my dreams, set my goals, work hard, and make my dreams come true. That's what I choose to do, with each new day."

January 22

"I know that the secret to unlocking the doorway to my most positive future is my own self-talk and every thought I think each day. So I make sure that the messages I give to myself are filled with self-belief, self confidence, determination to succeed, and an absolute certainty that the best is yet to come."

January 23

"There is nothing that is possible that I cannot accomplish when I put my mind to it, and decide to do it. I am living a life of unlimited possibilities. And all I have to do is decide what I want to achieve, put myself into action, take the first step, then keep moving, and refuse to give up! That's how dreams come true."

January 24

"I will reach my weight-loss goal. I refuse to stop, give up, or give in, even for one day. I have a goal to succeed, and I am reaching my goal!"

Self-Talk Tip #4

Your Self-Talk Today Is Creating the Person You're Going to Become Tomorrow

Imagine what would happen if the way you talked to yourself today would create the person you'd meet in the mirror tomorrow. That's exactly what's happening, but many people aren't aware of it. You're wiring who you're going to be, in the future, into your brain right now.

Once you know this, you can change or improve who you'd like to become, and you can start the process by the thoughts you think.

Do you weigh the weight you'd like? Or, are you as happy as you'd like to be? Would you like to be smarter? Do you want to do better in your relationships? How about your job—are you the best you can be at what you do? What about your talents and skills? Are you living up to what you could have been, or have old programs convinced you you're not as good as you'd like to be? None of those things are accidents. They're the result of your programs. And programs can be changed.

The self-talk you practice today will create the 'you' you're going to become tomorrow. That means that most of life really isn't the result of blind luck or fate. It's up to the programs you create. And those programs are entirely up to you.

January 25

"I can't wait to go for it. Just imagine what I can do. My plans, my goals, my future, anything I choose—creating my fitness, reaching my weight-loss goals, and feeling good about myself. I can't wait to make things happen. So today, I'm not waiting. Today I'm going for it!"

January 26

"I practice seeing myself as I most want to be. I see myself being healthy and in great shape. I see myself accomplishing great things. I see myself being at peace and happy with my life. The more I see myself that way, the more I create what I see."

January 27

"I make good choices. I choose to be healthy and fit. I choose the right friends. I choose what I do with my time. I choose my goals, and I choose my direction. And I choose to do my best each day. I choose my attitude, I choose my self-talk and I choose how I think. Today and every day, I make good choices."

January 28

"My life is on target, I have a great fitness goal, I know what to do, I'm taking action, and I'm doing everything it takes to reach my goal. Today I use the self-talk that says, *'I'm on top, in tune, in touch, and going for it!'*"

January 29

"I was born with unlimited potential, so I choose to always get better and continue to grow. I choose to live up to my unlimited promise. I choose to become the me I was intended to be."

January 30

"My life is good. The moment I think about it, I realize how true that is. I'm here, I'm alive, and I have unlimited possibilities in front of me. Every day I'm here is a blessing and an opportunity to live up to my best. Once again, starting today, my whole life is in front of me, and I know that my life is good."

January 31

"My attitude is always up to me. Whenever I feel down, I choose to change my attitude and get myself feeling up again. No matter what's happening in my life, I choose to think up, be positive, feel confident, and believe in the bright promise of my future. When I choose to have a winning attitude, my whole world changes for the better."

Self-Talk Tip #5
What is the Difference Between Positive Self-Talk and 'Affirmations'?

The terms "self-talk" and "affirmations" are sometimes used as synonyms for one another, but they're not the same. Affirmations are positive statements most often used in spiritual or holistic expressions such as *"I am one with the divine universe"* or *"I am guided to seek the greatest serenity in all things that I do."* They may be similar, in some ways, but they're not the same as self-talk as we're using it here.

Unlike affirmations, self-talk gets very specific, very clear, direct, and to the point: *"I get things done. I take action. I set clear, specific goals. I work at them, and I reach them."* Or, *"I get up at 6:15 each morning."*

Good self-talk messages are instructions to your brain, telling it exactly what you choose to do, with detailed action steps that put you in control. When it comes to the mental computer that runs your life, you don't give it affirmations, you give it directions. Conscious, positive self-talk messages are directions for your brain.

February 1

"When it comes to creating my best possible future, I have patience. I am willing to work for, and wait for, the positive results of my efforts to come into my life. I think ahead, plan ahead, and stay with it. And I'm willing to be patient and wait for the results."

February 2

"When someone says "I cannot," I answer "Why not?" When someone says "It's impossible," I answer that nothing is any more impossible than I believe it to be. And today, with my incredible attitude and positive self-talk working for me, anything good is possible."

February 3

"There is nothing that can stop me or hold me back from my own success in being fit, being healthy, and weighing the weight I want. When it comes to my future, what counts most is me, and the next choice I make."

February 4

"I take the time to appreciate the many blessings and the wonderful opportunities I am given each day. I may get busy taking care of the day at hand, but I am never too busy to be thankful for what I have."

February 5

"I consciously create peace, calm, and quiet contentment in my life. During each day, I practice stopping for a moment, take a few slow, deep breaths, recognize that I am on my journey, glad to be here, thankful for the moment, and at peace with my day and my life."

February 6

"By taking control of my life, my thoughts, my health and my actions, I also control and conquer any unnecessary limitations I had placed on myself in the past."

Self-Talk Tip #6

Reading Self-Talk Every Day, *Resets* Your Brain in a Positive Way

Reading positive self-talk every day does three important things for you:

#1. Adding the right self-talk to your day sets up your brain in a neurologically *healthy* way. When you practice positive self-talk, you tell your brain to think that way throughout the day. Doing that resets your focus, and that makes your brain work to make each day more positive.

#2. Reading daily self-talk opens your mind to positive new ideas that the self-talk messages inspire. The practice of reading self-talk will help you create the habit of attracting positive new thoughts, and through repetition, begin to create new programs. That makes you more aware of what's going on in your life and ready to take action in the right direction.

#3. Reading daily self-talk gives you an immediate attitude adjustment. The more positive your self-talk, the better the day you're likely to have. Your self-talk directs your attitude, and your attitude directs your day. If you want to have more good days, start and end each of them with positive self-talk.

February 7

"I choose to create abundance in my life. Always healthy, always good, always more than I need, and always enough to share with others. With my attitude, the choices I make, and the actions I take, I create abundance in my life."

February 8

"I have learned the truth about myself, and I like what I have learned. I now know that I am capable of doing anything I choose to do, and I choose to be in control of me."

February 9

"I choose to make today an incredible health and fitness day! I'm here, I've got everything I need to make today one of my best days ever, and I've got an entire world of positive opportunities in front of me!"

February 10

"Today l choose to be in a great mood all day, smile a lot, learn something new, uplift someone who needs encouragement, spend time improving myself, eat right, be healthy, enjoy my day, and really like who l am."

February 11

"Problems don't bother me. When a challenge comes up that requires my attention, I take care of it. I focus on the problem, I study it, I make sure I understand it, I deal with it, I take the necessary action, and I move on."

February 12

"I make sure I'm headed in the right direction. I keep looking forward and I keep moving. I don't stop, doubt, or hesitate. I concentrate on the goal, keep my focus, stay positive, take action, and make every day count."

Self-Talk Tip #7
Your Weight and Your Self-Esteem

Healthy weight and positive self-esteem go hand-in-hand. As a general rule, the higher your self-esteem, the fewer problems you will have with weight. That doesn't mean that every problem with weight is attributed solely to low self-esteem, but the two are almost always found together.

"Self-esteem" is a sometimes misunderstood concept. It doesn't simply mean 'loving' yourself; it means your complete estimation of yourself—a photograph of who you believe yourself to be, in every area of your life.

We continually adapt ourselves to look and act like the picture of ourselves we carry in our minds. If your internal photograph of you is hurting, or lacking, or tells you that you're not as good in some way as others around you, your self-esteem will reflect that belief back into your life each day.

The most important thing you may ever do to live happily at the healthy weight you want, is to work first at building a healthy picture of you in your mind. Use the right self-talk, and use a lot of it. Build yourself up, create the picture of the healthy, happy, you, and practice seeing that picture of you every day. Focus on that picture. That's the picture that will help you win.

February 13

"Today I choose to believe in my dreams, focus my vision, set my sights, get a clear, bright picture of the goal I've set for my perfect weight and fitness, and take a giant step forward. Today is the day I grab my goal and go for it!"

February 14

"Any doubts I might have had about any weight-loss goals I've set in the past were nothing more than old programs of doubt that weren't true in the first place. Today I have faith, I have drive, I have determination, and I have belief. *I can do this and I know I can.*"

February 15

"Today I know what I want. I have a clear picture of my goal to weigh the healthy weight I choose. I replace my doubts with determination, conquer my fears with faith, stop putting off my own success, and take action now."

February 16

"Today and every day, l choose to use the gift of choice. Each day l choose what l think, what l do, what l eat, what exercise l will get, and even what my attitude will be. l know that life is a series of choices, and l choose to make my life work right. l choose to choose."

February 17

"I make sure that I take time for myself. I help others, and I love them and care about them, but I also care about me. I make sure that I rest, relax, and do the things that create health and fitness in body, mind and spirit."

February 18

"My whole world is in front of me today. I have countless opportunities. I have unlimited potential. I have an incredible attitude. I have non-stop belief. And I have *me*. It's a perfect day to love my life and go for it!"

Self-Talk Tip #8

What Stops Us From Being That Amazing Person We Dreamed About Becoming?

When they're young, most people dream about doing something special with their lives. A lot of those early dreams *could* have been reached, but they weren't. What went wrong?

Research tells us that most of our success is the result of the way our brains get "wired." Our beliefs about ourselves are the result of the wiring we get from others, and eventually from our own self-talk.

When we're young, and believe anything is possible, our brain hasn't yet been wired with what we *cannot* do. It just accepts us as being unlimited, with little or no disbelief to get in the way of our dreams.

But all too soon we're told—by people around us—what *won't* work and what we *can't* do, and our brain starts to wire those messages in as though they're *true*—even if they weren't really true when we first heard them. In time, many of those disbelieving messages become permanently wired into our once unlimited brains. And we replace our dreams with limitations. We could have done almost anything, but we got wired to do something less.

Thanks to positive self-talk we can change that. Because we can *change* our programs, and rewire our brains with the right self-talk, we can bring some of those old dreams back to life—or create new dreams that are just as good. And this time we won't let anyone take them away.

February 19

"I choose to reach my weight-loss goals. I never give up and I never give in. Instead of letting problems stop me or hold me back, I look forward to my fit and healthy future, I deal with any problem that comes up, and I keep moving!"

February 20

"I keep a clear picture of my health and fitness goals in front of me at all times, and today especially. I see each of my goals. I believe in my ability to reach them. I take every action step I need to take. And I make sure I achieve them."

February 21

"I know that my attitude is entirely up to me. So I choose to keep my attitude up. Even when things seem down or difficult, I know the one thing I can always count on is my own bright, positive, winning attitude. No matter what, I keep my attitude up."

February 22

"Today I vote '*yes*' to my weight-loss success. I was born to succeed; That's how I think. That's what I do. That's how I live. And that's who I am. When it comes to success, I vote *Yes!*"

February 23

"When l want to accomplish something that's important to me, l give myself the self-talk that says, *'l have the dream. l have the goal. l have the faith. l have the drive. l have the determination. And l have what it takes to reach my goal.'*"

February 24

"I have made the decision to take control of myself, my health, and my fitness —and that includes how I look and what I weigh."

Self-Talk Tip #9

Having a Talk with Yourself Can Change Your Day.
It Can Also Rewire Your Brain.

Some people used to think that talking to yourself was a sign of mental illness. We now know that having a conversation with yourself can not only be *healthy*; it can literally rewire your brain and make it better.

The problem is, most of what we say when we talk to ourselves is the same old programming, usually negative, that we were used to giving ourselves in the past. Research shows that most of our unconscious programs are the negative kind. So out of habit we continue, unconsciously, wiring and rewiring ourselves in the same, negative way.

But now imagine changing that, and having an entirely *different* conversation with yourself—using positive self-talk—the kind of conversation that tells you what you *can* do, and what *will* work. Do that like you mean it, and you can actually feel the difference physically.

Of course, while your day will usually get better, it takes more than a few talks with yourself to rewire your brain, and repetition is the key. The more often you talk to yourself with the right self-talk, the better it works. And the more you begin to rewire your brain in the positive.

February 25

"Living up to my potential is up to me. Doing great is my choice. So I never underestimate myself or what I can do. When it comes to what I can accomplish, and the positive good I can achieve, I never count me *out*. I always count me *in*."

February 26

"I know that every good weight-loss plan starts with a specific, healthy, desired weight, and nonstop, daily determination to reach that goal. I have the plan, I have the goal, I have the determination, and I will succeed."

February 27

"I know that I am responsible for creating the dreams I choose to live in my life, and I am responsible for making them come true. So I visualize the dreams, follow my plan, take the next step, and make my dreams happen."

February 28

"I keep myself motivated. Each day I visualize myself reaching my fitness goals and living my dream. I know what I want to achieve, I take action, I work my plan, I stay with it, and I get things done. I am focused, filled with energy, and very, very motivated!"

February 29 (For Leap Year)

"Sometimes, when my dreams are high enough, and the challenges are big enough, it takes a leap of faith to get me there. But I have my plan, I know the goal, I take the leap, and I get there."

Self-Talk Tip #10
3 Surprising Ways Self-Talk Changes Your Life

#1. When you practice the right self-talk, you set yourself up for a better future. Repeated self-talk forms new neural pathways in your brain. Those pathways form the blueprint on which your future ideas and actions will be based, and the results of those actions lead to your successes and accomplishments. Rule #1: *Your self-talk sets up your future.*

#2. Your self-talk changes how you see the world. When you're down, it's hard to believe anything can work right. When you're feeling your best, the world changes. You feel in control of your life—and when you're up, so are your successes. That's because how you see your day affects your day. Rule #2: *Your self-talk changes the world around you.*

#3. Your self-talk changes how *other* people see you. Think of a day when you were unstoppable, feeling great, and on top of the world. How did other people react to you? When your self-talk is on top, so are you. And that's how people treat you. Rule #3: *The world treats you like you treat yourself.*

March 1

"When I have a goal as important as my fitness or my health, I never listen to the negative doubts of others. I have learned to listen only to the positive words they offer—and to the powerful, positive, winning new words from myself."

March 2

"I choose to believe. Along with my spiritual beliefs, and the faith I have in the promise of the future, the one belief I have that will always direct my life for the better is the belief I have in myself. When it comes to seeing the best in myself, I choose to believe."

March 3

"Today I choose to make my life work right. What I don't like, I change. What I can't change, I deal with and find a way to turn it into a positive. What I do like, I focus on, give it energy, and create more of it. Today, I make the choice to make my day an incredible day in every way."

March 4

"Each time I read these words I am even more aware that I have taken a positive, super healthy new direction in my life--and I am determined to stay with it!"

March 5

"I have great value. I have exceptional worth. I have many positive qualities. I have a reason for being, and purpose in my life. I count, and I make a difference. That's me. That's what I choose to accept. And that's how I choose to be."

March 6

"When it comes to losing weight and keeping it off, I am my own best motivator. I believe in myself and I can do this!"

Self-Talk Tip #11
Getting Used to 'The Super You'

When you first begin practicing positive self-talk, the way you express yourself could sound strange to the people who know you. People who are unfamiliar with self-talk may wonder what's up with you, or why you're talking that way. They're not used to 'the super you.'

If you make practicing self-talk a goal, and make it part of your life, you *will* sound different. Your words and your attitudes will make some people think you've gone through an unexpected change in your personality, when you've just gone through a change in your self-talk.

When you start practicing positive self-talk, some people will love it, and they'll support you. But some may not. (Seeing you become suddenly highly positive could worry family or friends who don't understand.)

The most important thing about changing your self-talk, however, is not what someone else thinks about it. Practicing positive self-talk is about what *you* want to achieve: your goals, your attitude, how you feel each day, and living up to the individual you choose to be.

When you change your self-talk, don't worry if it sounds strange, or what other people might think. Just keep doing it. The results will speak for themselves.

March 7

"Who am I, and what can I do? I am a non-stop, go-for-it, confident, upbeat, positive, self-believing, super-achieving, always caring, dream-sharing, uplifting, forward thinking, future-building, life-embracing, success-creating go-getter with unlimited potential and endless opportunities in front of me. That's who I am, and just watch what I can do!"

March 8

"Changing my day for the better, by thinking right, thinking up, and choosing to succeed, always works best with practice. So I practice looking at my life each day in the most positive, possible way. The more I practice, the better I get, and the more successful days I create."

March 9

"Today and every day I actively focus on my weight-loss goals. The more I focus on reaching my goals, the more I believe in reaching them, and the better I do."

March 10

"How do I make my life work? I care about others, I believe in myself, I make sure my attitude is always up, I believe in the future, I set clear goals, I'm willing to work for what I want, I always have faith, and at the end of each day, I always know what I want to accomplish tomorrow."

March 11

"I take the time to rest, relax, unwind, recharge, regroup, reassess, rethink, reset, and recommit. Then I refocus my thoughts, redouble my energy, put myself into action, hit the ground running, and go for my goal!"

March 12

"I'm so blessed, in so many ways. I see the morning sun, I see the people I care about, I see the day with its endless opportunities. I see all the chances I'm given to live up to my best. And every day I remember the words: 'I am so blessed, in so many ways!'"

Self-Talk Tip #12
Self-Talk as 'Comfort Food'

Is there anything that can take the place of comfort food? Until the perfect, fat-free, emotionally-supporting, security-giving chocolate or confectionary bonbon is created, there may be nothing safe that will replace it.

With the exception of self-talk.

We seek comfort food out of habit, or when we're lacking something emotionally satisfying, or when we feel insecure. That's the child in us wanting to be safe, happy, protected, and feeling good again. When the world around us doesn't deliver that safety and security, something to eat often will.

The next time the moment arises that you find yourself circling the kitchen, or opening the chocolates and forgetting your goal to lose the weight and keep it off, ask yourself the question: *What am I missing? What am I replacing? What do I need?*

Practicing positive self-talk won't take away every craving overnight. But if you want to reach your goal, the more you practice, the more comfort you will find. Within the right self-talk, you will begin to find a new sense of self, with safety, security, and self-control. It may not give you the immediate gratification of a bonbon, but it could give you a new life.

March 13

"I practice being mindful of my own thoughts by consciously asking myself the question, *'Why did I just think that thought?'* Practicing being mindful of my thoughts puts me in control of own self-talk, and my positive direction in life."

March 14

"Today is the day I decide to go for it. Today is the day I reset the goal. Today is the day I make the choice to make it happen. Today is the day I put myself into action. Today is the day I do it."

March 15

"If I ever have doubts, if I'm unsure about what to do next, I immediately reread my weight-loss goals. I review the steps I need to take, make the choice to take action, believe I can do it, and take the next step."

March 16

"When I think of myself, how I want to look, and how fit I want to be, I have a clear picture of what I'm going for. I visualize it. I never let it out of my sight. And I go for it!"

March 17

"Every day I make sure that I keep myself at my mental and physical best. And that means I keep myself motivated, seeing the me I choose to be, and doing everything I need to do to reach my goal."

March 18

"I choose to be in control of my emotions, especially the negative emotions of anger, hurt, guilt, blame and fear. I choose instead to practice having happiness, understanding, acceptance, confidence, and joy. And what I practice, is what I live."

Self-Talk Tip #13

You're Probably More Intelligent Than You Thought

There is a very good chance you're smarter than you think you are. Or, at least, you can be if you choose to be. In a few short years we won't even recognize the standard IQ tests we relied on in the past. (How could a single test, administered perhaps only once during your youth, accurately define the intelligence of a brain that changes constantly and literally rewires itself every day of your life?)

If, as we now know, your brain changes based on the input you give it, then it makes sense that if you give it the right, new input, your useable IQ will grow along with it. At a minimum, the ability to use your intelligence more effectively will grow.

The new understanding that your real IQ is not genetically set from birth gives you the opportunity to reset your own useable intelligence. With that knowledge, and knowing that your self-talk plays a vital role in reprogramming your brain, it makes sense to practice self-talk and other activities that improve your mental acuity. And that's an intelligent thing to do.

March 19

"I live today for today in a positive, health and fitness way. I learn from yesterday and I prepare for tomorrow, but today I focus on today, and I make every moment count. Now is the time, this is the moment, and today is the day. When it comes to getting fit, today is the day."

March 20

"To learn the habit of setting goals, I start with a small goal. I write it down. I set the date, list the obstacles, write the action steps, and start with the first step. Then I stay with it, and reach the goal."

March 21

"When I want to reach my weight-loss goals, it's not where I've been, what hasn't worked in the past, or how hard I thought it was to reach the goal that counts the most. The only thing that counts now is my attitude today, and what I choose to do next."

March 22

"I never try to just get by or do as little as I can. I take my weight-loss seriously and I give it everything I've got. I'm not just 'kind of' doing it—I'm winning!"

March 23

"I have decided to be my #1 *believer*. I know that people who make the choice to believe in themselves always do better than those who don't. So every day I choose to believe in myself and work at improving myself in some way. Each day I do this, is a day that works."

March 24

"Every great book, and every wise person who speaks of success, all tell me that my success will always get down to how much I believe in myself. If that's true, and I believe that it is, then my success in this life, and in this moment, is truly up to me."

Self-Talk Tip #14
With Positive Self-Talk, You Choose
a Future that Works

So much of the story of positive self-talk is filled with hope. Here's an example:

Is it possible that you get to choose your future, and make it a future that works? According to research in neuroplasticity and self-talk, that's exactly what you get to do. It's not where you've been or what's happened in your life up to now that will write your future—it's what you choose to do next, and the self-talk you use that will get you there.

Many people go through their entire lives believing in the old programs that tell them their destinies are mostly set, and there is little they can do about it. They are taught to believe that luck and the whims of the world around them are the most important determinants of what happens to them—as though they are pawns in a game of chance over which they have no control.

But breakthroughs in the field of neuroscience tell a different story. We now know that much of what happens *to* us is the result of programs in our brains that literally set us up for success or failure, in almost anything we do.

The result of the research is that we now know our futures are not solely up to the whims of the world around us. You get to choose a better tomorrow, make sure you have the mental programs that will take you there, and create a future that works.

March 25

"I know that people who have little belief in the future see life as difficult, filled with problems, without opportunity, and nowhere to go. But because I practice believing in myself and in my future, I know that my life is full of opportunities, I can achieve anything I choose, and I have everywhere to go."

March 26

"I remember the dreams I had of who I wanted to be, and the things I wanted to do with my life. No matter how much time has passed, and what has happened between then and now, I still choose to have my dreams, and I choose to bring my dreams to life."

March 27

"Today is another good day to practice patience. I have patience. I know that having patience is essential to success, and an important quality in my life. I practice having patience every day, in the smallest things and in the biggest things, every chance I get."

March 28

"I do well with my weight-loss goal because I know what I want. I have a positive fitness plan to follow. I know the steps to take. I take action. And I do every positive thing I need to do to get me there. Because I know what I want, follow my plan, and stay with it, I always reach my goal."

March 29

"Getting my weight in shape counts. This is important. How I look and how I feel affects everything about me. So I do everything I need to do to weigh in at my best, be healthy, feel great, and love my life.

March 30

"It isn't only what I dream about that counts. If I want to make something happen, I also set a real goal. I write it down. I identify the obstacles, I write out the action steps, and I get started. My dreams count, but it's the goals I write down, and take action on, that make them happen."

March 31

"Getting in shape is about today and doing it now. This is the time, this is the place, and now is the moment. Today I choose to reset the goal, have the vision to see it, the faith to believe it, and the determination to achieve it."

Self-Talk Tip #15

Who or *What* is Really Doing Your Thinking For You?

Behavioral research suggests that over 90% of everything we think is an unconscious replay of the programs that are already wired into our brains. Many of those programs are false, negative programs, and most of them were put there by someone else.

How much of your thinking is really your own? Probably less than 10%. That is, until you begin consciously practicing positive self-talk, taking control of your own programming, and wiring your brain with the kinds of programs that *you* choose to put there.

When you practice positive self-talk, your thoughts will still come from programs that are wired into your brain. But this time *you* will be the one who is consciously wiring them in. This time they'll be the positive and helpful kind. And this time they'll be right.

April 1

"Today I choose to turn any doubts I've had into the powerful, positive self-talk that says, *'I believe in myself! I can do this, and I know I can!'*"

April 2

"I know my weight depends on how I see myself, and what I say when I talk to myself. So I visualize myself the way I most want to be, and I create that 'me' with the self-talk that helps me get there."

April 3

"Right now I choose to change my life for the better. With every healthy choice I make, I am creating the successes I'm living today, and the future I will be living tomorrow. In everything I do, I choose to find my best."

April 4

"I have a great attitude about my weight, my fitness, and my goals. Because I choose to have an attitude that is positive, staying on my plan is easy for me."

April 5

"I know that people who achieve, first choose to believe. So when it comes to weight-control, I make sure that my attitude is up, positive, confident, and going for it! Today especially, I choose to believe in myself, and believe in the winner that I am. I can do it, and I know I can!"

April 6

"I am motivated. I am determined to eat right, look great, and live healthy. I motivate myself every day, and it shows."

Self-Talk Tip #16

Positive *Self-Talk* is More
Than Positive *Thinking*

Positive self-talk isn't just about positive thinking; it's about managing *all* of the thoughts that are being wired into your brain.

Unlike basic 'positive thinking'—looking at the world in a generally positive way—positive self-talk could be compared to the flight program the navigator types into the onboard computer on an airplane. Whatever direction the navigator types in is the direction the plane is going to fly. Direction, course, altitude, speed—everything the airplane's onboard computer needs to know to take the plane safely to its destination. It's not just a positive thought or two—*it's a detailed set of program instructions that will fly the plane to its objective.*

Positive thinking, by itself, is a good thing, and it helps you look at the world in a bright and healthy way. But positive self-talk, like the navigator's instructions to the computer, is more specific. The right self-talk identifies every step you need to take to get where you're going, sets the course to get you there, keeps you uplifted and motivated on the journey, and makes sure you arrive safely, and on time.

April 7

"Today I get a clear picture of who I want to be. I decide what I need to do to improve myself in some way today, make the choice to do it, and make sure that every choice I make today will help me become the incredible person I want to be tomorrow."

April 8

"Each day I visualize myself being my perfect weight. I see myself living the benefits of being healthy, fit and happy. And the picture I see is what I create."

April 9

"Instead of wishing, wanting, waiting, or hoping for things to get better with my weight and fitness, I make things better, every day. My future is not based on hoping for the best; my future will always be the positive result of how I think, and what I do each day."

April 10

"I am in control of my thoughts, my activities, my weight, my fitness and my health. And that puts me in control of so many positive, healthy choices I make each day."

April 11

"When it comes to losing weight and keeping it off, it all gets down to what I believe about me. If I think I can do it, I can. If I believe I have it, I've got it. If I really want it, I go for it! If I truly believe in me, I'll prove it!"

April 12

"I see healthy change as a natural part of life, the next pathway to my positive future, and the opportunity to grow. In any change that comes my way, I look for the opportunity in the change, I find a way to learn and grow because of it, and I make it work."

Self-Talk Tip #17

Positive Self-Talk Changes the
'Shape' of Your Brain

People who practice thinking positively, physically reshape their brains by changing what they think.

Research has shown that thinking *positively*, physically grows new neurons in the *left* prefrontal cortex of your brain, and boosts your ability to see alternative solutions. That increases your chances of making better choices—and being more successful.

(Tap your forehead above your left eyebrow. That's where a lot of your positive possibilities get their start. The correct self-talk grows more neurons there.)

Meanwhile, people who think *negatively* grow more neurons in the *right* prefrontal cortex of their brains. That causes them to close off opportunities and ideas that could have helped them succeed. When you're thinking negatively, your brain is also processing potential solutions at a slower rate. Why? Because it's busy dealing with fright, fight, or flight, instead of focusing on the positive solutions that could have solved the problem.

If your self-talk is positive, you're not only wiring in new neural pathways that change how you feel, how you look at life, and how successful you're going to be at just about anything; you're changing the structure of your brain in the right way.

April 13

"When it comes to my goals and my dreams, I let nothing or no one take them from me. I hold the key that opens the door to my own unlimited future. That future is mine. What I do with it is up to me."

April 14

"Can I weigh the healthy weight I want? Yes I can. Can I become the physically active person I want to be? Yes I can. Can I really be healthy and fit? Yes I can."

April 15

"I choose to dream, to believe in, and to create, the most remarkable, healthy positive future for my world and for the life I'm living. I may be practical and down to earth, but when it comes to creating my own future, I also choose to dream, and I'm always willing to believe in the best."

April 16

"Every day I reaffirm my goal to be healthy, eat right, be active, and do the right thing.

April 17

"I take time for me. I know that my life works best when I set aside time that is just for me, so I plan it, and I do it. I make sure that I am strong in spirit, well-rested, have peace of mind, and feel good about myself. To do that, I take time for me."

April 18

I choose to make every day a health and fitness day. From the moment I awake, to my last thought at night, I choose to make health and fitness a major part of my day.

Self-Talk Tip #18
Seeing the Glass as Half *Full*

Behavioral researchers have shown that when it comes to your goals, you only reach what you can see. Or, put another way, you only reach the goals you can clearly imagine. That's true of the biggest and the smallest things in life. Overall, if your brain can't 'see it,' you probably won't get it.

The 'glass' is, of course, a metaphor for what we believe or what we imagine to be. Since the brain will work hardest at helping you get those things that you can most clearly imagine, if your glass is 'half empty' and you can't see the possibility of getting what you want, your brain won't help you get it—*you're wiring your brain to believe it won't work.*

Seeing the glass as half empty stops you from seeing the opportunities that are in front of you, and programs your brain to act as though you won't get what you want. The result is, you usually won't.

When you practice seeing the glass as half full, you literally switch on the part of your brain that searches for alternatives and possibilities. So instead of your brain being busy being negative—and making sure something won't work—when you change your brain to think in the positive, it gets busy looking for ways to make it happen.

April 19

"My day today is up to me! So l choose to fill my day with high energy, have a great attitude, know that things are going right, and create a positive outcome in everything l do. My day today is up to me, and l choose to make today an incredible day!"

April 20

"I never let problems or challenges hold me back or stop me. Instead of letting problems get me down, I keep myself up! I keep my eye on the goal, take the right action, believe in the best, have faith, move on, and make my day a winning day."

April 21

"I don't fear winning at weight as some kind of battle I have to fight. I see maintaining my right, healthy weight as the natural way for me to live."

April 22

"I don't wait for success with weight-loss to just 'happen,' or quietly 'hope' for a healthier body to come my way. When it comes to my healthy success, I choose it, I create it, I go for it, and I make it happen."

April 23

"I choose to weigh the right, healthy weight for me. I choose it, I live it, and I make it happen."

April 24

"Today I choose to have a great attitude about my weight-loss goal! How I feel about today, and what I do with it, is really up to me. So I choose, right now, to have an incredibly good attitude, feel great about myself, decide to go for my goal, and make today one of my best days ever!"

Self-Talk Tip #19
You Were Born to be Successful

Negative self-talk tells us that we deserve *less* than the best. When it comes to love, money, talents, skills, luck, job promotions, good looks or almost anything we'd *like* to have, but may not think we can get, it's our own negative self-talk that's telling us what we don't deserve.

The truth is a different story. You were born to succeed. All of us were. No exceptions. You were designed to excel. Like the flowers of the field or the birds in the sky, one is not created to succeed while another is created to fail. When it comes to life itself, we were designed in every way to grow, learn, overcome challenges, become stronger, and reach the highest levels of personal growth and fulfillment. That's true of all of us.

Blessings aren't handed out randomly or unfairly—more for some and fewer for others. Blessings are given out in direct proportion to *our intention of receiving them, our willingness to work for them, and our willingness to believe in them.*

The real you, the true you that you were born to be, deserves every blessing you choose to imagine and accept. And that gets down to your self-talk and your beliefs about yourself. You will accept and create what you believe you deserve.

Check your self-talk. Make sure you've got the right programs of self-worth and deserving. When it comes to how much you deserve, no matter where you've been or what has happened in your life so far, you were born to have an equal share in the universe. You still have it.

April 25

"I am not alone. I have my life, my dreams, my goals for healthy weight and fitness, and my determination to succeed. And I make sure I always surround myself with my undying faith, others who believe in me, and an unstoppable belief in myself."

April 26

"I don't worry about losing weight or keeping it off. I spend my time being fit, eating right, being active, and getting healthier every day."

April 27

"I know the great truth: that my life, and what I do with it each day, is up to me. I know that I alone am responsible for what I think, what I do, and what I say. I practice being in control of my life, myself, and my weight, every day, in every positive way."

April 28

"I take time to improve myself both physically and mentally, and I work at getting better at anything I do. I may be doing okay so far, but just watch me. Because I'm working at improving myself in some way every day, I will become even better tomorrow."

April 29

"I can always count on me. I set my goal, I eat right, I get the right exercise, and I stay with it."

April 30

"I will not be stopped when other people doubt me. I will not be held back by other people's fears. I have my goal; they have theirs. I have a road that is mine to follow, and I choose to believe in myself, follow my path, and keep going. And because I do, I will reach my goals, and I will win."

Self-Talk Tip #20
Self-Talk in Sports

Self-talk can help you in virtually any area of your life. But a good way to measure the results is in studies with athletes.

As just one example, a study of the use of self-talk in a cycling competition showed an *18%* increase in endurance among bicyclists who practiced self-talk techniques for two weeks prior to the event. *Eighteen percent* is a dramatic and game-changing increase, when even a 2% increase in endurance can win the race.

In the test, the control group, which used self-talk only during the tests, with no previous self-talk practice, had *no* increase in endurance. Meanwhile, the members of the group who practiced self-talk two weeks in advance were literally *rewiring their brains* to create more endurance during the race.

As science is repeatedly showing us, self-talk, when used correctly, is an effective tool that can wire new, helpful, neuron pathways in the brain. If practicing the right self-talk can give you that great an edge in sports, imagine what it can do in the rest of your life.

May 1

"Every day I make sure I laugh often, feel good, do something creative, find a way to play, have fun, feel the joy, and keep the child in me alive and well."

May 2

"I never live my life based on the negative opinions of others. I set my goals, I live my life, and I choose to listen to me."

May 3

"The most important asset I have is my attitude. With a simple, self-directed change of mind, I can instantly alter how good or bad I feel, the direction of my day and how it will go for me, how well I will deal with anything that happens, what bothers me and what doesn't, how thankful I am, how much enthusiasm I have, and how other people will see me. And all of that will come from my attitude."

May 4

"If at any time I backslide in reaching my weight-loss goal, I stop, reset the goal, ask myself what I have learned, tell myself what I will do differently next time, and thank the mistake for giving me the opportunity to get it right."

May 5

"If I make a mistake, I forgive myself. But I immediately get back on track, reaffirm my will to succeed, boost my determination, and go for it!"

May 6

"I never blame others for my missteps. I take responsibility for everything I do. When I've made a mistake, I accept it, I learn from it, and know I will do better the next chance I get."

Self-Talk Tip #21
Positive Self-Talk Can Lower Your Stress

The next time you see stress coming, before it takes over your day, there's something you can do. Stress is a product of your mind. You're not imagining it—it's very real—but your mind is creating it. That's good news, because if your mind is creating your stress, you can also tell your mind to *un*create it. Stress is a symptom of your attitudes being at odds with something that's happening in your life. The internal conflict creates a negative emotional response, and like a bad habit, stress steps in.

How you feel about something determines how you react or respond to it. And who is in charge of how you feel about anything? You are. Your *programs* are the source of your stress, and you can override the programs that are causing the problem. If you want to defeat the stress, immediately create a new message to your brain:

"I had hoped it wouldn't rain today, but it's raining, somebody needs the rain, and I can live with it and still have a great day."

"I have a lot to do, but I'll do the very best I can. I'm thankful for the job, and glad to be doing it."

"I know that families sometimes argue, but I love my family and I know tomorrow will be a better day."

When your world is not entirely in your control, there is one thing you *can* control, and that is your attitude, and the stress that comes with it. And the one way you can always control your attitude is with the right self-talk.

May 7

"Controlling my weight and my life is easy for me now. I enjoy smaller portions, smaller bites, and a slower, more relaxed way of eating."

May 8

"I have set a goal and I am staying with it. I have turned 'meal time' into 'achievement time.'"

May 9

"It isn't life's problems that count the most. It's how I choose to deal with them, that counts. Problems may be challenges, but I choose to deal with each of them in the most positive possible way. I'm glad to be here, and problems are not a problem for me."

May 10

"Today I choose to look for the positive, practice smiling, do something really healthy, learn something new, take some time for myself, and do something for someone else."

May 11

"I take time for others; but I also take time for myself. I listen to what others have to say, but I also listen just as attentively to anything I have to say. I care about others, but I always remember to show myself that I truly care about me. I believe in others, and I let them know it; but I make sure to let myself know, that I also believe in me."

May 12

"What I eat, the weight I choose, and the goals I reach, are up to me. Others may help, but no one else can create my success for me—my success is up to me."

Self-Talk Tip #22

Self-Quiz: Are You a Positive Self-Talker?

Whether you're just getting started as a positive self-talker, or you've been at it for years, here is a simple quiz that will tell you how well you're doing.

- How often do you notice your own self-talk during the day? Often___ Occasionally___ Almost never___

- Do you edit what you might have said or thought, and replace it with better self-talk?

- Instead of arguing or disagreeing, do you stop, think, and recognize the self-talk of the other person?

- Do you consciously work to improve your own self-talk?

- Do you see positive self-talk as a short-term idea for your personal growth, or do you see it as a life-long solution?

- Is everything you say, especially to yourself, stated in the healthiest, most positive, way?

You'll know just from answering those few questions how well you're doing at becoming a positive self-talker. Wherever you stand, just keep practicing the right self-talk. Doing that will create one of the most helpful habits you will ever have.

May 13

"If there's something that's holding me back, I don't just wait for it to go away. I figure out what it is, I take action, and I deal with it."

May 14

"Today I am unstoppable! I have my goal, I know what to do, and today I choose to do it! I am strong, upbeat, capable, clear-thinking, determined, smart, sure of myself, thinking positive, heading for the future, full of energy, filled with enthusiasm, ready to win, excited about my life, and ready to make it work!"

May 15

"I know that life is incredibly good, and filled with endless opportunities. So every day I look for the good, choose the best, and do every positive thing it takes to reach my goal. My success, with my weight or anything else, is not an accident, it is a choice."

May 16

"I make sure I keep my balance and perspective. When things don't go my way, I let myself know that *I can deal with this, I will get past this, and tomorrow is another day.*"

May 17

"Who says I can't do it? Who says I can't reach my goal? Who says I don't get to reach any fitness goal I set? If you want to know who I really am, just watch me. I reach my goals. I live up to my dreams, and I make them come true. That's who I am and that's what I do."

May 18

"I am never, at any time, tempted to take one more bite than I should. I am strong. I am capable of reaching my goal . . . and I am doing it!"

Self-Talk Tip #23

Liking Yourself at the Weight You Weigh

Here's some good advice: Don't wait until you've reached your goal, or until you're 'perfect,' to like yourself. Like yourself today.

It's easy to confuse not liking your weight with not liking your *self*. You're not your weight. You're a wonderful individual working on a goal. The more you keep the true picture of your positive qualities in mind, the more likely you are to stick to your goal, keep working at it, and reach it.

Getting in shape takes effort and often hard work, but it should be fun, a time to feel especially good about yourself, and liking who you are right now, today, even before the goal is reached. If you put off feeling good about yourself for some later time, you miss all those days of appreciating life and enjoying the moment.

It's that choice, to enjoy being 'you' *now*, that adds the magic of positive enthusiasm to your efforts. Liking yourself every day, appreciating the moment and enjoying the journey, can make the difference between just working at a diet—and happily reaching your goal.

May 19

"Okay world, get ready! I'm here, I'm prepared, I'm filled with energy and enthusiasm, and I'm going for it! You might as well be on my side and help me get there, because with you or without you, I've made the positive choice to win!"

May 20

"I never let any of my 'limitations' stop me or hold me back. I know that I have the ability to reach any goal I set, and there is no limitation that can stand in the way of my success. After all, I created my limitations in the first place, and I can let them go."

May 21

"By creating the picture of my own health and fitness in my mind, I make it happen in my life. I follow the simple steps of: *dream, goal, plan, action, perseverance* and *achievement.* That's the way success works. That's the way I choose to make my life work."

May 22

"The more times I think the thought, the more I program the message in my mind, and the more I create it in my life. So I always think and repeat good, healthy, positive thoughts."

May 23

"Even the thought of eating something that is not good for me, serves to remind me of my own winning healthiness."

May 24

"If I were to give a gift to myself, it would be the gift of health, fitness, the right weight, a great feeling about myself, a great attitude, and positive new beginnings. And that is the gift I choose to give to me."

Self-Talk Tip #24
Finding the Incredible You

As you read the positive self-talk messages in this book, there is something you should know about you: *You were born to achieve.*

You were born with unlimited promise and potential. No matter what has happened in your life up to now, the potential you were born with has never gone away. It may have gotten covered over for a time with the experiences and the difficulties of life, but the incredible person you were born to be *never* goes away.

Old, negative programs in the brain make us believe that we are not capable, not good enough, or smart enough, or talented enough, or destined enough—but all of those programs are wrong.

You have, today, everything you need to make your life work in an exceptional way. If you wonder if that's true, that's just the old, out-of-date, negative programs trying to convince you otherwise.

Do this: Practice positive self-talk. While you're practicing, ask yourself the question: *Would I like to be the person that my positive self-talk is showing me?*

If that's the person you want to be, and if you continue to talk to yourself in the most positive, believing way, your life is going to change. The change will be glorious and amazing. *You will be finding the incredible you you were born to be.* And you will have brought it all to life with your dreams.

May 25

"When I ask myself the question, 'What am I doing with my life today?' I always know the answer. I am thinking *up*, being certain of who I am, sure of what I want, helping others, reaching my goals, and doing everything I need to do to make life work . . . today especially!"

May 26

"I choose to create fitness, health, and wellness in my life. Along with my goals and my choice to take action and make each day count, I also practice having patience, staying calm, creating serenity and peace of mind, and making my day a quality day in every way."

May 27

"I am in control of how I think and what I eat, and it shows! I have a goal, I'm staying with it, and I'm doing great!"

May 28

"I am responsible for my choices in life. I know that what I make of myself, what I weigh, how I look, and how fit I am is up to me. So I set my course, I make good choices, I follow my path, and I take personal responsibility for every step I take along the way."

May 29

"The attitude I choose to have, day after day, will do more for me than anything else that happens each day. How I look at my life right now, today, and how I feel about it, is entirely up to my attitude— and my attitude is entirely up to me."

May 30

"I have patience. I know that my important goals of healthy weight and healthy fitness may take time to reach, but I am determined to succeed. So if I ever doubt, I immediately reset the goal, and I stay with it."

May 31

"I set clear, specific goals. I write each goal down on paper, along with the date I intend to reach it. I list the obstacles to reaching the goal. I then write the action steps I'll take to deal with each obstacle. I take action on each step. I review my goals for five minutes every morning. And I reach my goals."

Self-Talk Tip #25

Why Do People Who Practice Positive Self-Talk Do *Better?*

Over all, people who think in a positive, optimistic way, and who actively practice using positive self-talk, tend to do better in dealing with problems than people who are negative. Why is that?

The answer is based on neuroscience. Thinking negatively shuts down the creative, open-minded qualities of the brain. Positive "self-talkers" are open to more alternatives, so they have more choices when it comes to solving problems and dealing with life. They literally see more solutions than people whose horizons are limited by negative thinking.

Neurologically speaking, positive self-talk 'wires in' the idea of giving yourself more choices, and being willing to see the possibility of succeeding. While negative self-talk convinces you to stop trying, practicing positive self-talk keeps you looking for a more successful outcome, until the right solution can be found.

June 1

"Today I'm going for it! I know my goal, I know what I want to do, and I know that all I have to do is do it. So I choose to take control of my day, stop the excuses, put myself into motion, take action, put all of my energy into making it work, and refuse to stop until I reach the goal."

June 2

"Every day I choose to make the best of any situation. No matter what, I practice having a winning attitude, a 'can-do' spirit, and a non-stop belief in making things work. And what does practicing having a great attitude do for my life? It makes it better in every way."

June 3

"Weighing the weight I want and being fit and healthy is my choice. Creating fitness and healthiness for myself is entirely up to me."

June 4

"When it comes to my weight and health, I never wait for someone else to lift me up, set my course, or get me moving. I know that my success is up to me. What I believe, is what I achieve. And every day I choose to believe in the best and create my success."

June 5

"I choose to be healthy in every way. I choose to eat right, get the nutrition I need, rest well, exercise often, be productive, look for the good, avoid negative people, avoid negative habits, help others, always think in a positive way, smile a lot, believe in the best, and always picture myself and my future, living a life of health and success!"

June 6

"It's not 'luck' that helps me reach my goals; it's how I look at it. I choose to see the bright, find the good, believe in a positive outcome, and always have faith that I will overcome the challenges and succeed. And because that's how I choose to look at my fitness goals, I win!"

Self-Talk Tip #26
From *Self-Talk* to *Success* in 5 Steps

One of the subjects the book *What to Say When You Talk to Your Self* discusses in detail is the process by which changing your self-talk leads to actual changes that take place in your real life. Here it is in a nutshell:

1. When you change your self-talk, you change what you **believe** about yourself.
2. When you change what you believe about yourself, you change your **attitude**.
3. When you change your attitude, you change your **feelings**.
4. When you change your feelings, you change your **actions**.
5. When you change your actions, you change your **results**.

To test this for yourself, think of something in your life (or in yourself) you'd like to improve. Then focus on that area of your self-talk for two or three weeks. When it comes to that subject, give it your full attention, and completely change *all* of your self-talk about that subject—to the positive.

When you do that, and stay with it, you will change your belief, your attitude, your feelings, your actions, and your results.

June 7

"Today I choose to focus on my weight-loss goals, get a clear picture of what I need to do next, make the decision to take action, get my attitude in shape to get myself in shape, put myself into motion, and make today a health and fitness day!"

June 8

"I am always mindful of being healthy and reaching my goal. Because I'm mindful, I listen to what I say, and I also listen carefully to my thoughts. Because I'm mindful, I'm in control of what I think, what I eat, the exercise I get, and how well I'm doing."

June 9

"I have fun losing weight and keeping trim, and I'm really proud of the great job I'm doing."

June 10

"When it comes to my attitude, I'm up! When it comes to my weight-loss goal, I'm going for it! When it comes to staying with it, I'm there! And when it comes to making my day an incredible day, I'm on it, I've got it, and I'm making it happen!"

June 11

"When I change my Self-Talk, I change what I believe about myself. When I change what I believe about myself, I change my attitude. When I change my attitude, I change my feelings. When I change my feelings, I change my actions. And when I take the right actions, I create my success."

June 12

"When I have doubt, I choose to have faith and believe in the best. When I feel I just can't win, I refuse to give up or give in. When I'm not sure about reaching my goal, I remind myself that I can do this. And when I wonder whether I should continue, I always choose to take one more step forward."

Self-Talk Tip #27
The Real Cause of Extra Weight

The reasons people give for having problems with weight are many, but most of them get down to just three things: Attitude, eating, and exercise. All three are important, but it's the first reason—*attitude*—that is the foundation for almost all weight problems.

Why is that? Because your attitude controls the fork and spoon. Attitude makes you hungry when you shouldn't be. Attitude overrides your better judgement and makes 'one more bite' okay, and does the same thing again, time after time. Attitude creates the need to eat the wrong thing, or more than necessary, and then attitude justifies the extra eating, and tells you it's okay.

All of that attitude, of course, is the result of programs that tell you how you feel about everything you do. Your programs create your attitudes, and if they're the wrong programs, those attitudes can defeat every common sense diet or fitness program you try.

That's why practicing positive self-talk helps you get healthy and fit; self-talk wires new attitudes into place in your brain. If your attitudes are causing you to struggle with weight, solving the problem starts with getting better programs. The right self-talk will help you do that.

June 13

"Of all the people who help me, influence me, or guide me in any way, the one person who has the most control over my thoughts, my actions, and the direction of my life is the person I spend the most time with each day. The one person who holds the key to who I am and who I will be, is me."

June 14

"When it comes to getting fit, and weighing the weight I want, I'm up to the challenge. I'm good at reaching goals. This is an important goal to reach, and I'm definitely up to the challenge."

June 15

"I'm making today a healthy day in every way. I choose to eat right, get the activity I need, and focus on fitness. That's how I reach my goal."

June 16

"I have been given the incredible gift of being me.
So I choose to live up to the promise only I can fulfill.
I have so much to discover, and so much to live; so
much to offer, and so much to give. And every day
I choose to live up to my fit, healthy best, and to
become the me I was created to be."

June 17

"I do my best when I feel good about myself—physically and
every way—and how I feel about myself is always up to me. So
right now I take a good look at the real me, and choose to like
who I see. I can always get better, and with my weight-loss goal
I will, but I like who I am and I'm glad to be me."

June 18

"I am a person of exceptional quality. I have skills,
talents, abilities, and potentials that make me special in
so many ways. That is the real me as I was intended to
be. How do I know? That's the way God made me in
the first place, and God makes winners, not mistakes."

Self-Talk Tip #28
How Self-Talk Works

Your brain needs a lot of healthy programs in order for you to succeed or do well in life. Self-talk is a way for you to get positive new programs wired into your brain. It's based on neuroscience—on how the brain works—but it isn't hard to understand:

Your brain records every message you give it. The part of the brain that records those messages doesn't know the difference between something that is *true,* and something that is *false.* Positive or negative, bad or good, your brain just records it, and then acts on it. Any message you send to your brain *repeatedly* (by reading, speaking, or listening) gets wired in, and your brain acts on it as though it's *true*—whether or not it was true to begin with.

Giving your brain the right self-talk messages physically wires your brain with positive, new neural pathways that in time become the new you —but with better programs. Your day-to-day success is based on the number of positive neural pathways that get wired in.

The more you practice using the right self-talk, the more healthy, new neural pathways you wire into your brain.

June 19

"When I'm on a healthy weight-loss plan, if I ever stall
I immediately restart. I get right back on schedule
eating right, getting fit, and following my plan—and
I do it now!"

June 20

"I don't mind it if others question my weight-loss goals
or think I can't reach them. I know that real winners win
by following their greatest dreams, rather than listening
to the negative opinions of others. So I don't give up,
and I don't give in. And because I keep believing in
myself, I win!"

June 21

"I practice living each day in a peaceful, calm, and mindful
way. The reason I do that is because it's a healthy, mature,
and intelligent way to live—and it makes every day better."

June 22

"I can't wait to greet the day each morning. I have so many positive, healthy goals, dreams, and possibilities in front of me, and I choose to make my dreams come true. So every day I wake up, think up, get up, and go for it!"

June 23

"When it comes to improving myself, I never allow other people's doubts, criticism, or lack of vision, to stand in my way. I choose, instead, to set my own course, follow my own path, believe in myself, have my own vision, and make every day an incredible day."

June 24

"I alone choose every thought I think. I alone am responsible for the direction of my day. I may be surrounded by the love, help, and support of others. But I alone must choose my path, and I alone will find my way."

Self-Talk Tip #29
The Right Self-Talk is also
Practical Self-Talk

The right kind of self-talk is positive, but it's also practical. Positive self-talk helps you see the world in a brighter way, but it also makes sure you are realistic, clear-minded and level-headed. With the right self-talk, you don't ignore problems or challenges—you deal with them. You don't pretend everything is rosy; you see life for what it is, but you're better equipped to handle it.

When you read the self-talk on these pages each day, at first glance it could seem like the picture of life the self-talk shows you, is too good to be true.

But read on. You'll also find self-talk that sounds something like an internal drill sergeant; it tells you to knuckle down, be responsible, work hard, take action, do it now, stop complaining, keep going, and refuse to quit. Great self-talk, and very practical.

June 25

"Because I have a goal to be fit in every way, I refuse to worry, or let the challenges of the moment, or the problems of the day get me down. I'm here, I'm alive, I'm alert, I'm awake, and aware, and I'm ready to make today a successful day in every way!"

June 26

"I choose to live my life by choice, not by chance. My success each day, each hour and each moment, is not up to luck or fortune; it is up to the choices I make. And because I choose success, I choose to make good choices."

June 27

"Changing my life for the better, by thinking right, thinking *up*, and choosing to weigh the right, healthy weight, always works best with practice. So I practice looking at life in the most positive possible way, every day. And the more I practice, the better I get."

June 28

"I am attractive in many ways. I attract others to me. I attract their interest, I attract their positive attention, I attract their friendship, and I attract their belief. I attract the very best in everyone. Therefore, I am attractive!"

June 29

"I know that at any time, on any day, I can choose my attitude. And if I'm really determined to have it, that's the attitude I will have. So I choose, right now, today, to have an attitude that is positive, focused, healthy, upbeat, successful, and going for it!"

June 30

"It's not my parents, my DNA, or my circumstances that control my weight; it's me as I choose to be. And I choose to control my weight."

Self-Talk Tip #30
The Powerful Practice of 'Editing' Your Self-Talk

One of the three key steps for changing your programs is 'editing' what you think and say. Editing your self-talk is extremely important, and once you get the hang of it, it isn't difficult to do. (For all three steps to changing your programs, see Self-Talk Tip #43.)

As an example, when you're about to say or think any negative self-talk like, *"I can't remember names,"* stop yourself! Don't say it. Instead, turn it around and say, *"I'm good at remembering names. I care about people, I notice them, and I remember their names."*

That may not be true the first time you say it. But keep in mind that positive self-talk messages are showing your brain how you *choose to be,* even if you're not there yet. If you stay with it, and continue to give yourself the correct new self-talk every time the opportunity comes up, in time you will have wired that new truth into your brain, and in practice it *will* be true.

Do the same with anything you think or say that could be working against you. Change *"I'm never on time,"* to the opposite: *"I'm always on time."* Change *"I just know it's going to be another one of those days,"* to *"It's going to be a great day, and I'm going to make it that way."* Instead of telling yourself *"It probably won't work anyway!"* turn it around and say *"I can make this work. I've got this one,"* and then make it work.

Enjoy editing your self-talk! With practice you'll get good at it. In time you'll believe it. It will be you, getting to know the real you that you were meant to be in the first place.

July 1

"When in doubt about any decision I make about my diet or my physical exercise, I ask myself the question, *'What is the best choice for me right now?'* The best choice is always the healthiest choice for me."

July 2

"I say *'No'* to anything that is not healthy or right for me. Every day it is easier and easier to me to make the right choice. When I do, I am saying *'Yes'* to success."

July 3

"Even while I am focusing on my program of health and fitness, I am mindful of my day, each day. I take time to stop and smell the roses, and remind myself why I am here. Each time I do, I remember how important my health and wellness are to me.

July 4

"Because I am taking such good care of myself, I have more energy, enthusiasm and vitality than ever. Life is exciting, and I am really enjoying being me."

July 5

"I take time for myself, sometimes do little or nothing for a time, and I get the rest and healthy replenishment that I need. I also know that having a goal and taking action improves my life, and I make sure I create plenty of positive action to move me forward and reach my goal."

July 6

"I'm good at taking care of the present, but I also take time to practice looking into the future and seeing myself as I most want to be. I may not control or direct everything that lies ahead, but the clearer the vision I create of my own healthy future, the better I do at making it work."

Self-Talk Tip #31

The Right Self-Talk is never "Pollyanna Thinking"

Some people confuse positive self-talk with being 'Pollyanna positive.' The right self-talk is very positive, but the two kinds of thinking are very different.

Positive self-talkers always look for the best alternative, but they are also practical and realistic. Good self-talk takes into account being practical and having your feet firmly on solid ground. Being aware, being realistic, and being responsible, are hallmarks of good self-talk.

The Pollyanna thinker, on the other hand, instead of using self-talk that looks for and creates the right avenues to successes, may rely on hopeful thinking alone, without the discipline of the practical self-talk that creates a firm foundation for the optimism.

When you practice the right kind of self-talk, go ahead, be optimistic. Expect the best. The rest of your positive self-talk will also make sure you're doing everything it takes to get you there.

July 7

"If I want to be healthy, fit, and weigh the weight I choose, I can get rid of the programs that work against me, clearly imagine the me I'd most like to be, and create the positive, healthy, future me. The only thing that can stop me, is me."

July 8

"The stronger I am, and the more I live by the healthy decisions I choose for myself, the happier and healthier I am."

July 9

"My weight and my health matter to me. So I take the time to determine what I want from my life. When it comes to getting myself in shape, I know what I want, where I'm going, and what to do."

July 10

"I make sure I have balance in my life. When I keep things balanced, I'm adding very important leveling to my life. When it comes to balance in anything I do, whether it is work, play, the food I eat, how I spend my time, the sleep I get, or the goals I set, I use the self-talk that says, *'Everything has a right amount, and I always create the right amount of balance in my life.'*"

July 11

"I'm sticking to my plan to get fit in every way, and because I am, I'm getting healthier every day. So I smile a lot. I am happy on the inside, and I am happy on the outside."

July 12

"How far can I see? I can see tomorrow, and see myself taking every necessary step to reach my weight-loss goals. How far can I see? I can see next month and next year, and see myself looking great. How far can I see? I can see my success."

Self-Talk Tip #32
Seven Rules for Rewiring
Your Brain

If you'd like to wire your brain in a more positive way, research in the field of brain neuroplasticity has identified seven rules for getting the best results. They are:

1. *Mindfulness*
2. *Choice*
3. *Intention*
4. *Focus*
5. *Repetition*
6. *Emotion*
7. *Belief*

Research shows that the more you choose exactly what you want to achieve, the more you pay attention to your thoughts and focus on what you want your brain to record, the more often you repeat the same message, the stronger you feel about it, and the more you believe in the outcome, the stronger you will wire it in—and the greater the chance you'll make it happen.

From *The Power of Neuroplasticity* by Shad Helmstetter, Ph.D.

July 13

"In choosing to lose weight and get fit and healthy in every way, most of the limits I see in front of me are the limits I created for myself. Getting rid of my limits takes practice and the right self-talk, and I make sure my self-talk shows me what I *can* do, not what I cannot. Because I choose to see beyond my limits, my success is becoming clearer every day."

July 14

"I love the joy of getting fit. I know that when I take the time to experience it, that joy is with me every day. And because I know I'm reaching my goal, I feel the joy, every single day."

July 15

"I choose to think about my weight-loss self-talk today, and be consciously aware of everything I think and say. Because I am mindful and aware, and because I'm making sure it's the right self-talk, I'm reaching my goal and getting fit."

July 16

"Having great self-esteem helps me reach my weight-loss goals, and I build my self-esteem every day. I am warm, sincere, and honest and genuine. I am all of these things and more, and all of these things are me. I like who I am and I'm glad to be me."

July 17

"Because I have learned to be kind to myself, I am always able to be kind to others. I care about myself, and it shows, and how I treat others is always a reflection of how I feel about myself."

July 18

"Life is becoming truly exciting for me. Not only am I reaching my weight and fitness goals, I am learning the joy of taking control of my own life."

Self-Talk Tip #33

3 Steps That Help With Weight-Loss

Here are three steps that will help you reach and maintain your best weight. No matter what diet and exercise program you're on, add these:

1. Make positive self-talk an integral part of your plan. Follow the daily self-talk in this book, and listen to recorded self-talk daily. This will help you believe in yourself and become your #1 motivator.

2. Write down your goal. You have to tell your brain what you want it to do. Write down a specific goal that tells you your desired weight, and the specific date you'll reach that weight. Read your goal at least once each morning and once each night, without fail. If you miss the goal a time or two, that's normal; reset it and keep going. If you want to lose or maintain weight, your brain has to know what you want it to do.

3. Add some form of yoga and meditation to your regimen. Positive weight control is both mental and physical. Practicing yoga and meditation helps you tap into a very powerful higher part of you that will give you insight, strength and encouragement as you travel on your journey to wellness.

July 19

"I believe in myself. I know that believing in me is a choice, so I choose to like who I am, be confident in my qualities, believe in my potential, and believe in the best outcome of anything that I do."

July 20

"To create success with weight control, I have decided to let go of those things which I had allowed to stop me or hold me back in the past."

July 21

"I choose to control unnecessary stress in my life by making sure that I exercise, practice good health habits, look at the brighter future beyond the problems of the moment, consciously bring myself to a quiet place of peace in my mind, and know that within me, all is well."

July 22

"Each night before I go to sleep, I ask myself the question: 'What did I learn today that will help me do better tomorrow?' When I do this, I keep myself aware of my personal growth, aware of my responsibility to myself, and aware of the endless opportunities to help me grow."

July 23

"Today I choose to concentrate on those things which help me take control of my diet and exercise, focus my efforts, and direct my life in a healthy new way. That's my choice today and every day."

July 24

"I refuse to be negative. I'm a realist. I deal with life, and I let negative things go. Anything that drains my energy or my spirit is not healthy to hold on to, and I give it no space in my mind or in my life."

Self-Talk Tip #34

When You Listen to Self-Talk, Here's How to Do It

If you want to learn new, positive self-talk faster, by listening to it, here's how to get the best results.

When you're getting started, it works best when you listen to the self-talk in the background, while you're doing something else. (Recorded self-talk sessions are usually from ten to twenty minutes in length.)

In the morning, play the self-talk *in the background* while you're getting ready. When you start your day with the right self-talk, you set up your day in the 'positive.'

Another time to listen is while you're doing something *physical.* Listen while you're walking, running, exercising, doing yoga, or working out. Listening while you're doing something physical is based on research that shows that our brains wire better or faster when we're physically active.

Another good time to listen to self-talk is just before you go to sleep at night. This is a great way to end the day, see yourself at your best, and get ready to take on tomorrow.

Repeat the self-talk session each day for one to three weeks on any self-talk subject you want to work on. This will give your brain the time it needs to begin wiring in the new programs you're listening to.

Listen to Self-Talk audio programs at selftalkplus.com.

July 25

"My attitude is my business, and what I do with it is up to me. My attitude, my mood, and my outlook on life are mine to choose, and no one else has the right to choose them for me. No matter where I am, what I'm doing, or who I'm with, my attitude is my choice, and it's always up to me."

July 26

"I keep the positive, healthy child within me alive and well. I find life full of exciting opportunities to live fit and feel great. I have endless dreams about my tomorrows, and I can't wait for the next day to come."

July 27

"I take the time to learn positive ideas for being fit and healthy. I find good ideas everywhere. I look for ideas that increase my interest in my own fitness. I am open to new ideas. I learn from them, and my life always gets better because of them."

July 28

"I practice using positive self-talk for weight-loss every day. Because I do, I have better days, I am happier, I think better, my attitude is brighter, I deal with problems and move past them, and I reach my goals!"

July 29

"When I have any problem with my weight or fitness that I think I cannot solve, I remind myself that I can. I learn everything I can about the problem, make a list of the possible solutions, write a list of the steps I will take to overcome the problem, and take the first step."

July 30

"I now control my time, my weight, and all my healthy activities. I know what my objectives are. I do everything I need to do to reach them, and I make progress every single day."

July 31

"Today I choose to find at least one thing that helps me reach my fitness goals, one thing that helps me grow, one thing to look forward to, and at least one thing to do that helps someone else."

Self-Talk Tip #35

Your Self-Talk Determines Your Attitude Each Day—and Your Lifelong Success

It's amazing how your self-talk, when you're consciously aware of it, can change your day. The secret of positive self-talkers is: You're going to go through the day anyway; but what you make of it is up to you. People who practice positive self-talk every day literally set themselves up for their days to go better.

How does your daily self-talk, day after day, affect your life-long success? That's just math. The right self-talk, practiced every day, multiplied by the next year, or five years, or ten, *is* going to make the difference between life being average and life being exceptional.

Living up to your best, and getting the most from every single day, will always come down to how you talk to yourself, and how you program your brain every day along the way.

August 1

"I know that no matter what the problem is, there is always a solution. No matter what obstacle I may be facing, I choose to look for the solution, find the answer, decide what I need to do next, take the first step, and deal with it."

August 2

"I choose to keep myself looking good, feeling good, taking action and getting incredibly fit! I like myself that way, and that's the way I choose to live my day."

August 3

"I know that there are unlimited opportunities in front of me. I have more possibilities in my life right now than I can even imagine. So today I look for the positive, keep an open mind, expect the best, and get ready for incredible things to come."

August 4

"I've got it! I have the goal, I have the opportunity, I have the tools, I have the reason, and I have the belief from others and the trust in myself. So I choose, right now, to make the choice to go for it and make it work!"

August 5

"I am the friend who urges me onward. I am the helper who won't let me stop. I am the believer who pushes me forward. I am the coach who puts me on top."

August 6

"When it comes to my goals, I never let the world outside of me have more importance than the world that lives within me. I know that my own thoughts, my own feelings, my own direction, and my own steps, will always be as important to me as the world I live in every day."

Self-Talk Tip #36
Better Self-Talk, Better Goals

The goals you set, if they're realistic, can only be as high as your expectations. And what you expect is always determined by your programs. That means that your self-talk creates the limits you put on your goals. If you want to set greater goals, you have to have the right self-talk to back them up.

Why do some people set a goal to travel the world, and actually reach the goal, while other people set a goal for something far less, or set no goal at all? It's because the person who plans to travel the world actually *sees* himself or herself doing it. That person has recorded programs that see the world-traveling goal as possible and achievable. The person without the goal is the person without the belief.

When you start practicing positive self-talk, it's a good idea to take stock of your goals. Write them down, so you know what they are. Then, after you've practiced the right self-talk for a few months, review your goals again. This time you'll find yourself resetting them higher. By reprogramming your brain to recognize what you're really capable of, your belief in yourself and your belief in your goals will have increased.

What goals could you set? What could you be capable of achieving if your internal self was completely on your side? The right self-talk will let you know that you are capable of much more, and reaching far greater goals, than you might ever have imagined.

August 7

"I stand up for myself. I know who I am, I know what I want, I know what I believe in, and I refuse to let anyone else tell me how I should live my life, or do my breathing for me. I care about others, but I live my own life, and I stand up for myself."

August 8

"By ordering less when I eat out, and by serving myself smaller portions at home, I keep myself aware of the importance of staying with my goal."

August 9

"Some of the qualities I admire most are: a great attitude; compassion for others; self-confidence; positive goals; belief in the future; a willingness to work; patience; and determination to succeed. Those are qualities I admire in others. Those are qualities that create success. And those are qualities I'm building in me."

August 10

"I never put off 'getting my life together' or becoming the 'super me' until some other time. The time to be the real healthy and successful me is now."

August 11

"I decide what I want, set a goal, work for it and reach it. I give to others, while I take care of myself. I live each day with joy and purpose. I work at becoming the incredible person I was born to be. And I create a life that works."

August 12

"I know that *procrastination* is a habit, and so is *getting things done* a habit. So I choose to create the clear, positive habit of doing what I need to do, and getting things done, on time and in the right way."

Self-Talk Tip #37

'Getting Physical' is Good
for Your Brain

You now have another reason to love exercising: Physical activity helps you grow healthy brain cells. Combining your self-talk practice with a good exercise program, such as aerobic activities, will actually help you wire your brain with healthy programs faster and stronger.

If you're on a treadmill or working out, instead of listening to music as a background to your exercise, listen to a session of your favorite recorded self-talk. Set a goal to do that for 10 to 20 minutes a day. Listen to the same subject each day for up to three weeks if it's something especially important that you're working on each day—weight loss, self-esteem, getting organized, etc.

When you combine the right exercise with the right self-talk, your brain's natural neuroplasticity gets an energy boost that improves connections between brain cells and enhances your brain's ability to wire in the positive new pictures of you that your new self-talk is creating.

If you're not listening to a recorded self-talk session while you're working out, you can still benefit by focusing on the positive self-talk you want to wire in. Either way, try replacing casual music listening, or a random, wandering mind while you're exercising, with strong, active, positive self-talk. When you come to the end of your session, you won't just have improved your body; you will have improved your brain.

August 13

"I give myself daily encouragement to reach my weight-loss goals. I give myself courage and strong self-belief. I keep myself up, and I never let myself down."

August 14

"I enjoy exercising now more than ever before. I have incredible determination and a non-stop positive attitude. I exercise, and—I like it!"

August 15

"I know that what I believe about anything, is always based on the programs I have stored in my mind. I make sure that the programs I have are positive, show me my best, and always lead me in the right direction."

August 16

"*I find time to listen in the stillness. I listen carefully to the whispers of my soul. I listen to the quiet voice deep within me that believes in me, and helps me walk along my path. And when I listen, it is clear to me that my life has a reason, with great value and purpose, and I am not alone.*"

August 17

"Every time I exercise I feel better about myself. I can feel my self-esteem growing even stronger, and I am really proud of myself for the great job I'm doing."

August 18

"I am in control of myself in every way, at all times and in all situations--especially when I sit down to eat. When I eat, my healthy self is always in control."

Self-Talk Tip #38

What to Do If You 'Fall Off' Your Weight Control Program

There may not be a single person ever who decided to lose weight and never 'fell off' the program. Even the best diets work only when our brains are wired to make them work.

Most of weight-loss or weight-control is in the mind. Weight is a *physical* thing, but it's controlled by a *mental* thing: your programs. Until you rewire your brain with the right, healthy programs, being in control of your weight will continue to be a challenge. And the biggest of those challenges is falling off the program, blowing the diet, backsliding, or just stopping entirely. If that happens, here's what to do.

What you *should* do: Start again. Get back up. Reread your goals. Practice self-talk. Keep doing it.

What *not* to do: If you blow your diet or slip, *never give up* or think you can't do it. You can. Falling off a diet is caused by old mental programs that told you you weren't up to it; or by *habits* (also programs in your brain) that haven't been updated to create the healthier you.

Keep going. You can do this. You can make it work. And your life will get better because of it.

August 19

"Whether eating in or eating out, I always enjoy eating less."

August 20

"I make sure that I add my own intention to anything I want to create in my life. I know that intention adds energy to my thoughts, and the more positive intention I bring to anything, the better I will do."

August 21

"I know that the right physical activity adds not only to my physical well-being, but to my mental strength as well. I make sure I am physically active, and I do everything I need to do to keep myself in the best physical condition. And that helps me feel better and think better."

August 22

"If there was ever a time for me to live up to my best, this is it! I am smart, capable, determined, full of ideas, filled with enthusiasm, and ready to make it work. So I have made the choice to reset my goals, believe in myself, expect the best possible outcome, get started now, and go for it."

August 23

"I never feel the need to finish the food in front of me. I eat only what is right for me, and not one bite more."

August 24

"Being in situations that put a lot of food in front of me is not a problem for me now. I simply say 'No!' to the food, and 'Yes!' to my success."

Self-Talk Tip #39

Visualization Changes Your Brain

When you visualize something clearly, your brain sees it as real. So if you want to imprint something in your brain, such as losing weight or some other goal you want to achieve, visualizing a clear picture of you attaining that goal will actually help your brain make it happen.

In a famous Harvard study of two groups of volunteers practicing a five-finger piano exercise, at the end of a week of piano practice sessions, both groups of volunteers showed an increase in neuronal growth in a specific region in their brain's motor cortex. This neuronal growth was the direct result of practicing the piano exercise for a period of time each day.

Here's the interesting part: one of the groups of volunteers had practiced playing the piano *only in their imagination*—without touching a piano! And they achieved results that were similar to those who had physically practiced on real pianos. Their practiced *visualization*, by itself, caused the new neurons to grow.

When you're practicing positive self-talk, make sure you're also visualizing the results you want to achieve. The more often you clearly visualize your intended result, the more your brain will see it, believe it, wire it in, act on it, and make it happen.

From *The Power of Neuroplasticity* by Shad Helmstetter, Ph.D.

August 25

"When I talk about myself, at any time, I always speak in the positive. That's not being self-centered, self-serving, or egotistical in any way. That's me, defining myself as I truly choose to be. The more I speak the best of myself, the more I wire it into my brain, and the more I create it in my life."

August 26

"I am getting fit, and I am doing this for myself, for my life, for my future, for my own self-esteem and for my own well-being."

August 27

"One way to lose weight that's easy and works, is *'Less food on my plate, and less on my fork.'*"

August 28

"I can change how I feel, the direction of my day, how well I deal with anything that happens, what bothers me and what doesn't, how positive I am, how much enthusiasm I have, and how much I will accomplish today. All of that, I can change."

August 29

"I am thankful for today. I am grateful for so much, and I remember to appreciate it and show it every day. I know that the more I count my blessings and recognize the good that comes to me, the more of it I create in my life."

August 30

"I enjoy sitting down to eat. Each time I do, I create a trimmer, happier, more self-confident future in front of me."

August 31

"I like the me I am creating every day. Doing this gives me health, fitness, the chance to feel really good about myself, and a wonderfully positive way to step proudly into the rest of my life."

Self-Talk Tip #40

Self-Talk, Weight-Loss, and Will Power

What could you do if you had all the will power you ever needed?

Your will power is created by your programming. It is wired into your brain. Will power is made up of 'belief' and 'determination,' both of which have been wired into your neural circuitry. What we call a force of 'will' is the result of how strongly your brain is wired to believe in something, and fight for what you want. You get all of that by having it wired into your brain.

Controlling your weight relies heavily on your *will.* Your willingness to stay with the right diet or intake of food, the right exercise, the right mental attitude—the success of each of these will depend on your will power.

The good news is you can create the will power you need. Your will power comes from the positive programs you have stored in your brain—the kinds of programs that give you more strength and a non-stop determination to reach your goal. And you can create those positive will power programs by the self-talk you choose and use.

Set a goal to increase your will power. Doing that one thing not only could make your weight plan work, it also will help you make the rest of your life work better.

September 1

"Because I'm reaching my weight-loss goal, I have less frustration, less unhappiness, and less disappointment in myself. And I have more of everything good."

September 2

"Why do I wait for something better? Why would I put off my future, when I can start right now? Today I choose to take control of my life, decide what I want to do next, set my goals, put myself into action, and take a clear, positive step *up* into my own, unlimited future."

September 3

"I make choices that keep me fit. I eat right, and I feel good about taking great care of myself. I know that my fitness starts with my attitude, so I make sure my attitude about my diet and the food I eat is healthy and positive, and always helps me live up to my best."

September 4

"I'm feeling great, thinking positive, making progress, and I'm so happy I made the choice to eat right, be healthy, and take control of my life."

September 5

"I have patience. I understand that some things take time. When I want to reach my weight-loss goal, I do it, but when I have to wait for time to run its course, I consciously take the time to understand, look forward with an attitude of calm and quiet, and appreciate the opportunity to watch my world work."

September 6

"I look great and I feel great. Looking and feeling good is one of the many rewards I receive for keeping myself fit and trim, and I keep myself that way."

Self-Talk Tip #41

Your 'Mental Apartment'

Imagine that you live in a 'mental apartment.' You've had the same old furniture for years. (The "furniture" is your old mental programs.) You got your hand-me-down furniture—your old way of thinking—from your family, parents, teachers, friends, and all of your past. It's old furniture. It's tattered and worn, but you're used to it, and it's all you know—it's your old way of thinking.

Now let's say you want to clear out your mental apartment, so you decide to get rid of all of your old mental furniture by getting rid of all of your old negative mental programs. So you take all of that old furniture out and store it out of sight in your garage.

The next morning you wake up to a beautifully empty mental apartment. No old negative furniture. No old easy chair of negative opinions. No old desk with drawers full of bad attitudes. No old television set spewing out negative programs. Your mental apartment is completely empty, and you realize you have nowhere even to sit down.

So what do you do next? After a while you go out to the garage and start bringing the *old* furniture back in! First you bring back in that old easy chair of "negative opinions"—the one you were going to get rid of.

(Continued on next page)

And then, later the same day, you bring in the old desk. That night, you bring back in the old television set.

Finally, after just a day or two, your entire mental apartment is filled back up with the same old, tattered, *negative* furniture that you were used to living with. Why did you bring it all back in? *Because you didn't have any new furniture to replace it with.*

If you want to get rid of the old negative furniture in your life, you have to replace it with something better. You have to get new positive "furniture"—new programs—or your *old* programs will come back in!

The new furniture is your new self-talk. Positive self-talk replaces the old negative furniture in your mental apartment with new, positive programs. When you learn the new self-talk, you change the furniture in your mental apartment for good. And that's the beginning of changing your life.

From *What to Say When You Talk to Your Self* by Shad Helmstetter, Ph.D.

September 7

"Today and every day, I take responsibility for myself. I get to determine how I look, how much I weigh, how fit I am, and how I feel. My weight and fitness are entirely up to me."

September 8

"I like to smile and I love to laugh. I make sure that every day is filled with joy, laughter, happiness, and feeling good about being alive and being me, in every positive way. I know that happiness is a very healthy habit, and I make sure my own happiness adds to my healthiness."

September 9

"I don't just stop and smell the roses. Every day, day after day, I stop and appreciate my life. I always remember that every day I live is a day filled with countless blessings, endless hope, and unlimited promise. Just to be here and to be me is an incredible blessing, and I know it and I show it every day."

September 10

"I am more than I could have ever imagined. I am responsible, and I always take care of my work and the day-to-day obligations of my life. But there is more to me than my work, or the daily details of my life. My possibilities are endless, my future is unlimited, and I always take the time to remember that I was also designed to soar with the eagles."

September 11

"I have fun losing weight and keeping trim, and I'm really proud of the great job I'm doing."

September 12

"My confidence in who I am, how I look, and how I feel, is reflected in everything I do. I'm confident about being fit and healthy, and the way I live my life proves it."

Self-Talk Tip #42
Making Weight-Loss a *Minor* Event

Important tip: Try not to make your weight control your 'major event.'

When it comes to weight control, do your best to not obsess or make it your most important focus. Life should be about finding your purpose, living and growing and achieving, not just about losing weight. The way to do that, and keep your perspective, is to make weight control a natural part of your life, the result of a few habits you can easily reacquire. Here's how to do that.

First, recognize weight control for what it is: a natural series of steps to getting better. That's all. Don't give it more credit than it deserves.

Focus on the positive benefits of overall wellness, not on the latest diet.

Practice the habit of putting small portions of the right kind of food on your plate, and then eating in smaller bites.

Practice positive self-talk that shows the healthy you as the true, natural you that you were designed to be.

Getting serious about weight-loss may seem like a big event, but practicing living a natural lifestyle of fitness and wellness will always be more important.

September 13

"I choose to practice the incredible art and skill of day dreaming. I get rid of the limits; go beyond the boundaries; and in my mind, fly to the farthest reaches of my imagination. When I'm dreaming of the endless universe of potential that surrounds me, I am wiring my brain to take me there."

September 14

"I choose to be happy working at and reaching my weight-loss goals. I know that being happy is a choice. And because happiness is also physically healthy, mood elevating, emotionally stabilizing, immediately uplifting, day changing, and contagious, I choose to be happy."

September 15

"I refuse to let set-backs or disappointments get me down. That's life, and life is exactly as good as I choose to make it. So I choose to see life in the most positive, optimistic way. I always deal with the challenges of today, but I never forget the unlimited possibilities of tomorrow."

September 16

"Because I am aware of the importance of my own health and fitness, I now spend my time doing those things that help me get more fit, in shape, and reaching my weigh-loss goals."

September 17

"I begin each day by concentrating and focusing on becoming my very best, positive, healthy self."

September 18

"I improve my health and fitness by liking what I do. I choose my work and enjoy it. Through my work, I take care of my family and home, I create service to others, and I find fulfillment that is rewarding and healthy in many positive ways."

Self-Talk Tip #43
Three Steps to Changing Your Programs

Your brain is built to constantly wire and rewire itself with new information; it is designed to change its programs if you tell it what to do. There are three steps you can take that will help you do that.

Step 1 – *Monitor.* Monitor means to listen to everything you say when you're talking to someone *else*, everything you say when you're talking to *yourself*, and even the thoughts you *think*. Consciously listen to everything you say or think.

Step 2 – *Edit.* You have the ability to edit and change anything you are about to say, or anything you're about to think. If what you were going to say or think next is actually negative self-talk, *don't say it. Don't think it.* Change it. Turn it around. Get it right. Turn it into a positive.

Step 3 – *Listen.* The best way to change old programs rapidly is by listening to new self-talk. It was by hearing the messages that were spoken to us originally that we received most of our old programming; it is by hearing the *right* self-talk repeated that those old programs are most easily changed.

People now listen to recorded self-talk sessions that are streamed to their tablets or smartphones. When you listen in this way, it's like learning a new language—by listening to it repeatedly until it gets wired in.

Self-talk programs to listen to on your smartphone or listening device are available at selftalkplus.com.

September 19

"I set my weight-loss goals. I review and work at the them each day. I see myself achieving each of them. And I reach them."

September 20

"When something happens that takes my weight-loss program off track, l make sure l don't let it stop me. l know that life happens, and not every day can be like l'd like it to be, but that doesn't bother me. l make sure my attitude is up, bright, and positive, and puts me right back on target."

September 21

"I practice being level, stable, and strong. I don't let everyday problems throw me or upset my day. When I face a problem, I deal with it and go on living. That's just life, and I love life and I'm glad to be here!"

September 22

"I practice having a happy, positive mind. The more optimistic I am, the more I train and prepare my brain for success. The more positive I see my life, the more determined I am to reach my weight and fitness goals, the better I do, and the more peace of mind and happiness I create."

September 23

"I could see each day and the world around me as down, negative, filled with problems, and nothing but obstacles and stress. But I choose, instead, to see each day as an incredible gift—a positive opportunity to live up to my best, get better every day, and be thankful for the chance to go for it."

September 24

"I refuse to measure my life by comparing myself to anyone else. I am living my life for my reasons, my purpose, and my destiny, not theirs. My goal is not to be as good as someone else; my goal is to be as good as I was created to be."

Self-Talk Tip #44

Why Do *Negative* People Think *Positive* Thinking Doesn't Work?

Negative people often see life as difficult and filled with problems, and tell themselves that positive thinking doesn't work.

When people see life as dark or difficult, they typically do so because their brains have become physically *wired* to see it that way. They can't see the benefits of being optimistic because their brains are wired to focus on the negative, and they seldom experience what true optimism feels like. So to them, life *is* negative, and because their brains are programmed that way, that's what they see.

Every input each of us gets repeatedly, physically wires our brains with positive, neutral, or negative programs—and most people who end up with negative wiring have no idea their wiring is negative or working against them. It's not their fault, of course; it's their programs.

September 25

"I listen to my regular, everyday voice. But I also listen carefully to the voice that is the higher, wiser part of me. To hear my wiser, inner voice, I make sure that I take the time, find the quiet, go within, be patient, and listen carefully. And the more I listen, the better my life works."

September 26

"When something goes wrong, or when I'm very disappointed, instead of thinking that life is against me, I choose to think about what is *right* with my life. I always find that when I add things up, there is far more positive than negative; life is working; and if I want things to go my way, it's up to my attitude, and up to me."

September 27

"I am good at telling myself 'no' to anything I should not eat. And when I tell myself 'no,' I mean it."

September 28

"I know that the path I choose to take in life is mine to find and mine to follow. I have guidance and support along the way, and some of my steps ask for the help and belief of others, but the path I follow is mine to choose and up to me."

September 29

"I replace the desire to eat something I should not eat, with the far greater desire to reach my goal, to live my dream, to like myself, to stay on target, and make today count."

September 30

"Avoiding something I should not eat is easy for me. I say 'no' to temptation and 'yes' to success."

Self-Talk Tip #45
Putting Off Taking It Off

It's natural to want to wait for some other day to change your lifestyle, eat differently, forgo the desserts and snacks, and say goodby to a food permissive lifestyle. Waiting until "next week" to begin getting healthy is not the exception, it's the norm.

The key to getting started, and then staying with it, is the magic word "goal." Setting a goal to lose weight or get fit is easy but important step. Writing a goal is essential for long-term success, and it's a great place to start. Even if you're already working at losing weight or keeping it off, write the following on a sheet of paper:

1. "My goal is to weigh _____ healthy, attractive pounds." 2. "The specific date I will achieve my goal is _____." 3. "The key obstacle to reaching my goal is _____ 4. "The action steps I will take to overcome this obstacle are (list the action steps you'll take.)"

It takes about 5 minutes to write out that simple goal plan. Writing it out and rereading it daily will help you get past putting off getting started. But even more important, when you start acting on it, you'll start to wire the new goal into your brain. That's where good habits begin.

October 1

"I never create unnecessary stress in my life. I spend no time being angry, holding a grudge, or adding any negative energy to my life. My brain is busy recording everything I think and feel, and I make sure my brain is recording health, wellness, and positive thoughts.

October 2

"When I have a weight or fitness goal that might seem difficult to me, I change the goal by changing the way I think about it. By seeing the goal in a positive way, I feel good about putting myself into action, and working at the goal every day."

October 3

"I deal with worry or fear by taking action or dismissing it. If the fear is something real that I need to deal with, I decide what to do next, and I take action. If the fear is something I should ignore, I dismiss it, put it out of my mind, and immediately replace it with something positive."

October 4

"People like me. They don't see the flaws I imagined that I had; they see the qualities I have that make me who I am. And when people like me, I don't question it, wonder about it, or think it isn't true. I just accept it: People like me."

October 5

"I have the strongest voice in determining the direction of my own future. And that includes what I weigh, and making my own health and fitness an important part of my life."

October 6

"I create quiet in my mind. No matter what is going on around me, I practice going within myself to find that special place of peace, harmony and quiet. And from that stillness comes strength, understanding, clarity, and balance. When I practice creating quiet in my mind, I create balance and wellness in my life."

Self-Talk Tip #46
The Gold-Colored Brain

Imagine that you have a simple outline sketch of your brain. You also have three colored pens with colored ink. One pen has gray ink, one pen is neutral, and one pen has gold ink.

Imagine that every time you have a thought of any kind, you make a small mark on the picture of your brain.

If your thought is a *neutral* thought, neither positive nor negative, you make a mark on the picture of your brain with the neutral colored pen.

If it's a *negative* thought, you make a mark with the gray, dark colored pen.

If it's a *positive* or healthy thought, you mark the picture of your brain with the bright, gold colored pen.

Imagine doing that with every thought you think each day. (It's estimated that we think as many as 12,500 to 70,000 thoughts in a day, so that would be a lot of colored marks!) At the end of just one day, what color would your brain picture be? Would it be mostly bright and gold, filled with positive; would it be neutral; or would it be gray and dark, and mostly negative?

What would the picture of your brain look like at the end of a year?

And the most important question is: What color will your brain picture be at the end of your life?

October 7

"When I encounter any problem in reaching my weight-loss goals, I always know that I am stronger than the problem. No matter what it is I face, I have the strength to stand up to it, and the determination to overcome it. So I deal with it, and I move past it."

October 8

"I see life as more than the world I live in each day. I see life as learning great lessons, filled with opportunities for joy, the chance to learn to love myself and others, the chance to be fit and healthy, and the time for me to become the person I was intended to be."

October 9

"No matter how big my goals are, I have courage. There are times I may be uncertain, but because I choose to have courage, I replace my doubts with determination, and I change my fear to faith. And that creates my victories."

October 10

"I enjoy making the decisions that affect my life. Making those decisions, and acting on them, gives me the confidence and determination to reach my weight, health, and fitness goals."

October 11

"I don't avoid the challenge, I face it. I don't fear the new, I embrace it. I don't mind the work it takes, I enjoy it. And I don't dread the day, I thank it."

October 12

"I have self-discipline. When I need to be in control of my attitude, my thoughts, my words, my actions, or my day, I have the right self-talk, and positive self-discipline to be in control of myself, and everything I think or do."

Self-Talk Tip #47

The Real Answer to Weight-Loss?

Some researchers say that the root cause behind a host of behavioral problems we act out is the lack of love in our lives. It's not hard to imagine that not feeling loved could cause someone to find solace in food. But it may the lack of a specific kind of love that could be the greater problem: the lack of *self*-love—truly caring about yourself.

Self-love manifests itself in self-esteem (how we see ourselves and believe ourselves to be); how well we take care of ourselves; how important our goals are; who we associate with most; how well our relationships work; what we do with our lives; and how successful we are overall. All of that is affected by how much we really like who we are, how much we love ourselves.

Caring about yourself is most apparent in how well you take care of yourself. People who develop a high level of quality caring about themselves also show their caring in how well they take care of themselves physically.

Learning to love or care for yourself has to be learned. If any lack of love for yourself, of any kind, could be causing problems with your physical heath, then the right self-talk can help. It takes time, but it can start you on the path of really liking, really loving, and taking care of the real you.

October 13

"I take pride in who I am, how I think, and what I do. I am never conceited and I never have false pride, but I take honest, healthy pride in my choices to be a quality person and live a quality life. And I am proud of the person I have chosen to be."

October 14

"I choose to take personal control of all parts of my life. I take care of even the smallest details that affect my happiness and success in any way."

October 15

"I never put things off, so I get things done. Because I'm taking control of myself, I make sure I am in control of all of my responsibilities—especially my health, my weight, and my fitness."

October 16

"I have focus. I practice paying attention to one thing at a time, and giving it my full attention. Because I have focus, I'm able to put all of my mental energy into anything I choose that's important to me, and I practice improving my focus every day."

October 17

"I enjoy being in control of my health and fitness. I now have more peace of mind than ever before. I am proud of myself for taking the time to take control."

October 18

"Being calm and in control of my life helps me reach my important fitness goals. So l keep my feelings and emotions in check. There are many things l feel strongly about, but l make sure that l am in control of my emotions, and they are never in control of me."

Self-Talk Tip #48

Your Destiny Is in Your Self-Talk, Not Your Genes

Scientists used to believe that almost everything about us was set—cast in stone by our genes. But now researchers have learned that your DNA is actually more like a blueprint, with control switches that are turned on or off by your experiences. That includes your *thoughts*. Your own thoughts can actually influence which of your DNA switches are activated and which aren't.

What the research suggests is that we may have far more control over our destinies than previously was taught. It was long believed that, although we weren't an exact carbon copy of our parents, the die was cast and there was little we could do about it.

In one way or another, our genes would determine our intelligence, our talents, and perhaps even how we looked at life. That would mean our potential as individuals would be the result of the genes we got.

It now appears that your self-talk may be one of the biggest factors in which of your DNA switches are turned off or turned on. The old adage that "the apple doesn't fall far from the tree" is *not* set. The exciting truth is, your destiny, who you become, and what you make of the life you've been given, is actually up to *you*––and the self-talk that directs your life.

October 19

"I'm good at dealing with conflict. I don't create conflict or seek it out, but when conflict comes my way, I immediately focus my mind on resolving it in the most positive possible way. I understand it, I deal with it, and I do everything I need to do to resolve it."

October 20

"I have learned to replace 'That's life, and there's nothing I can do about it,' with the words, 'That's my choice, and there is something I can do about it.'"

October 21

"I am very creative. I practice seeing things in new and different ways. I find alternatives and look for new solutions to any problem or opportunity. Being creative gives me unlimited chances to grow, learn, reach my goals, and make life a joyous place to be."

October 22

"I have vision. I see life beyond the moment, beyond the day, and into a future of endless possibilities. Because every day I practice having unlimited vision in anything I think or do, I am literally creating an unlimited future in front of me."

October 23

"I make good decisions about my health and fitness. I think about my choices with intention, focus, and clarity. I think about what is right, what is best, what the goal is, and what my intuition tells me. I study my choices, and I make good decisions."

October 24

"I am determined to reach my weight and fitness goals. When I have a goal and I'm doing what I know is right, I refuse to stop, give up, or give in. When I have an objective that is worthy of me and worthy of being fulfilled, I keep going until I reach it."

Self-Talk Tip #49

When Weight-Loss Isn't About Food

Weighing more that you want is often a symptom of something else—and it may have nothing to do with food. The real causes of weight problems typically include low self-esteem, lacking something else in your life, boredom, habit, not coping well with problems, self-sabotage, procrastination, or self-delusion. In spite of these real causes, most weight programs focus on food, when food itself is not the culprit; it's just the symptom.

The positive self-talk you practice should be made up of a healthy mix of messages that deal with the *real* causes, and not focus only on food or diet. The self-talk you're reading each day in this book goes beyond food or diets; the daily messages cover a broad base of subjects that are the real reasons for weight control problems.

When you're happy, totally in control of your life, fulfilled as an individual, working at reaching positive goals, and building healthy habits, you won't have to worry about weight. Resolving the real reasons for weight problems is where your self-talk focus should be.

The self-talk that will help most will not only be about food or diets. Practicing a broad base of positive self-talk that gives you the mental programs for building your personal strength of mind, body, and spirit, could become the only weight-control program you ever need.

October 25

"I focus on the goal, but I also focus on the results I'm creating. I look ahead and imagine the end results of my goal. The more I visualize the benefits I'm creating, the more energy I put into reaching the goal."

October 26

"When it comes to my own fitness, I enjoy the feeling I get when I take a stand, dig in, and refuse to accept anything less than what I want in my life."

October 27

"I'm good at overcoming adversity. No matter what the problem or challenge may be, I am determined to deal with it, overcome it, get past it, learn from it, and do better because of it."

October 28

"I have no habits that are harmful to me in any way. I get rid of any habit that could harm me, and keep those habits that build me up and improve my life. I choose to be positive and healthy, in every area of my life."

October 29

"I don't just plan to do great and incredible things with my life, I choose to create them and make them happen. I work at living a quality, healthy life, I think about what I want to accomplish, and I make sure I grow and improve in some way every day."

October 30

"I am strong, capable, and willing to do everything I need to do to reach my weight-loss goals. When it gets down to it, my success, is up to me. And I choose to go for it, create my success, reach my goals, and make my life work."

October 31

"My goal to lose the weight, get fit, and get it right, is not a minor goal to me. This is important, and today and every day, I stay with it. I am absolutely determined to reach my goal."

Self-Talk Tip #50

Extra Help for Practicing Self-Talk

When you're practicing positive self-talk, here's something that will help. One of the benefits of reading positive self-talk every day is that it gives you a pattern to follow—a style of self-talk you can adapt and apply to your everyday life. Good self-talk is a habit that will come with practice, and paying close attention to the self-talk messages you're reading each day will help.

Each time an opportunity comes up, practice rephrasing your thoughts, and what you say out loud to others, with the same kinds of word and phrases you read here. Every situation is different, but with practice you'll find that you're not only *talking* more positively in general, you'll also find yourself *thinking* that way, even when you're not focused on being positive.

Self-talk phrases like *"I choose to make today an incredible day,"* or *"I'm on top, in tune, in touch, and going for it,"* become more than words on a page; they become a way to pattern the rest of your thoughts throughout the day.

The goal, as a positive self-talker, is to be mindful of all of your thoughts, and consciously aware of the importance of your self-talk. The self-talk passages you read here can inspire a lot of good ideas, and, when you're getting started, they'll give you a helpful pattern to follow.

November 1

"I never let myself over-stress or get upset with the unimportant things in life. I take life seriously, but never more seriously than it deserves to be taken. I stay practical, always keep my balance, make sure my vision of tomorrow is clear and strong, and let the small things pass."

November 2

"From the moment I awake in the morning, to the moment I go to sleep at night, I am in control of what I do. And what I do helps me reach my health and fitness goals."

November 3

"I choose to wire unnecessary stress out of my brain and out of my life. I know that I control my thoughts. I can override any thought that doesn't belong, and each day I consciously choose thoughts that are peaceful, calming, positive, and helpful."

November 4

"When any thought that could lead me away from reaching my weight-loss goal tries to step into my mind, I immediately repeat the self-talk that says, *'I am in control of what I think. I choose to think positive, remember my goal, see myself reaching my goal, and become more determined than ever.'*"

November 5

"I like to play. I love to have fun. I love to be happy in the moment and be open to the amazing, positive world all around me. I'm serious and practical when I need to be, but I never forget that there is another world where I am full of fun, truly alive, and in love with life, just around the corner."

November 6

"I am wealthy in so many ways. I have more in my life at this moment than many people have ever dreamed of having. So instead of starting each day worrying about what I'm missing, I begin my day with gratitude for what I have."

Self-Talk Tip #51
A Helpful History of Self-Talk

The idea of changing our lives by changing our self-talk is very old. The Bible suggested the idea of self-talk in Proverbs 23:7, *"As a man thinketh in his heart, so is he."* Romans 12:2 said it even more directly: *"Be transformed by the renewing of your mind."* But the idea of using self-talk techniques for consciously reprogramming our minds would wait more than two thousand years before it would be accepted as scientific fact.

In the mid 1950s, following the 1920s-era writings of French pharmacologist Emile Coué, pioneering self-help authors such as Napolean Hill, Dr. Norman Vincent Peale, Dr. Maxwell Maltz and others, began to bring the concepts of positive thinking and conscious "autosuggestion" to the attention of self-help followers.

It was not, however, until the 1980's that self-talk, as it is used today, began to be generally understood. When researchers, using computer imaging technology, were finally able to see into the living brain, their research showed that because of the brain's ability to rewire itself, *self-talk*, practiced in the right way, could actually restructure the individual's brain with new neural networks.

Neuroscientists and behavioral researchers found that new input to the brain, such as specially-worded self-talk, could rewire and change not only the brain's physical structure, but the individual's attitudes, actions, and results as well. We had discovered that our *thoughts* physically rewire our brains—and the science of self-talk was born.

November 7

"The achievement of reaching my best weight, my best health, my best shape, and my greatest fitness, is an achievement that is worth every moment I put into it."

November 8

"I practice letting go, especially of any food or habit that could affect my diet or my fitness in any negative way. When it's time to move on or move past something in my life that should not be part of my future, I let it go."

November 9

"I make sure that every habit I have helps me create good health. If I do it, it's good for me. If it isn't good for me, I don't do it."

November 10

"When it comes to my own health and fitness, I choose not to compare my progress to the achievements of others. I choose, instead, to spend my time improving myself and finding ways I can do better, not so that I can rise above someone else, but so I can learn to rise above myself."

November 11

"I make every morning important. When I awake I always greet the day with gratitude for my life and appreciation for being here, this one day. Then I think about what I can do today to express my life in the most positive, helpful way, and make the world a better place because I am here, and get to live my life, this one day."

November 12

"When I reach a weight-loss goal, I reward myself in ways that are healthy and always build even more self-esteem."

Self-Talk Tip #52

Is Your Brain Wired to *Succeed*?

What really makes the difference in our lives? Why are some people successful, and other people are not?

Research tells us that our brains become wired for success or failure. As we grew, each of us got programs from the world around us, and many of those programs became 'permanently' wired into our brains. Those programs (neural networks in our brain) determine every thought we think and every action we take—which leads, inevitably, to success or failure in anything we do.

Since we were born, each of our brains has been recording, storing, and wiring in programs we received from parents, teachers, friends, and the world around us. If our brains got wired with enough programs that are positive and healthy, we live our lives in a positive, healthy, successful way. If, on the other hand, we got too many of the wrong kind of programs, we end up struggling—or failing—because of the programs we got.

If we receive too many of the wrong kinds of programs, we end up living with them and wishing things could be better—or we *change* them. Fortunately, our brains were designed to help us get rid of programs we don't want. That's why we practice self-talk—so we can change our programs. And this time we get them *right*.

November 13

"l dream big, but l'm also very practical. l set specific weight-loss goals, l put my plans in writing, and l take each action step l need to take to make my dreams come true."

November 14

"I find happiness when I begin my day with gratitude, find something that is meaningful or beautiful that I notice during the day, do something of value, and go to sleep knowing I helped someone else in some way that day."

November 15

"I think, act, feel, and live differently now. Right now, and at all times, I see myself in a whole new trim, fit, attractive way."

November 16

"If I ever stumble or stall, I don't wait for life to make things better, or for someone else to get me up and get me moving again. When I stall, I stand up and take one step forward. And then I take another step, and then another. Because I always keep moving, I am never stalled for long."

November 17

"When I sit down to eat, at any meal, I say to my self, *'I live best when I eat less.'*"

November 18

"I see losing weight, maintaining the right weight, and being fit and healthy as the natural way for me to be. It isn't a challenge, and I don't make it difficult; it is *natural.*"

Self-Talk Tip #53
Six Self-Talk Programs that Control
Your Weight

When you're practicing self-talk to get fit or control your weight, most of the new, positive self-talk that helps you will not be about food, diets, or even weight itself. It's often the *other* programs we have going in our lives that have the greatest influence on our weight. Here are the self-talk areas that influence fitness and weight control.

Self-Esteem. The programs you have that tell you everything you believe about yourself.

Taking Control of Your Life. The programs that put you in control, including control of your weight.

Health and Fitness. All of the programs that make up what you do and how you see yourself physically.

Relationships. Can be the #1 influence on choices about yourself, both emotionally and physically.

Personal Development. These are the programs that set up your choices to grow, or live up to your higher potential.

Quality of Life. These are among your most important programs, and they strongly affect your weight and health.

'Weight-loss' itself is not on that list. That's because weight and fitness are almost always the *result* of the self-talk programs that direct the rest of your life.

182

November 19

"Maintaining my weight is easy for me now. I've learned to eat right, exercise more, and keep my mind and my body fit and healthy."

November 20

"I listen to the quiet voice within me that is wise, caring, understanding, and always there when I choose to listen. I go to a quiet place in my mind, ask my question in clear, simple words, and wait for an answer. When I ask my question, wait with patience, and listen carefully, the answer always comes"

November 21

"I choose to listen to the earliest dreams of my childhood, and the unlimited possibilities for the life that I saw in my youth. So I stop now, see clearly the person I wanted to be, and ask myself the question: Have I lived my dream? And if I haven't, could I still?"

November 22

"Each day my self-talk wires my brain with a picture of the healthy, fit, person, in control of my life, that I choose to be. If I am 'down' on me, my brain will believe it, wire it in, and pull me down. If I am 'up' on me, my brain will be wired to help me succeed. The truth is, my fitness, like my tomorrow, is up to me."

November 23

"I am a person of quality. I have both dreams of unlimited potential and the humility to appreciate every blessing that comes to my life."

November 24

"I choose to have high self-esteem. I create more positive self esteem by living up to my best each day. When I do that, I feel better about myself, and I reach my weight-loss goals."

Self-Talk Tip #54

Taking Self-Talk to the Next Level

When self-talk was first introduced, it was recorded on cassette tapes for people to listen to. Today, people who want to take self-talk to the next level listen to specially recorded self-talk programs that are streamed to their tablets and smartphones.

The reason people listen to self-talk is because of the role of *repetition* in rewiring the brain. The most important rule of neuroplasticity for rewiring the brain is repetition. (We still remember the words to songs we heard when we were kids, when all we did was hear them played in the background. We can learn new self-talk in the same way, by listening to it.)

Recorded self-talk goes into depth to get to the heart of issues like weight-loss, self-esteem, relationships, stress, work, finances, etc. It rewires a broad group of programs in the brain that work together to create new attitudes and beliefs about the subject the listener is focusing on.

This kind of "super self-talk" is listened to daily, and it is clearly the daily repetition that does the trick; hearing self-talk repeated in this way forms new neural pathways that are imprinted in the brain. People listen while they're getting ready in the morning, or while they're driving in the car, or when they're at the office or around the house, or when they're going to sleep at night.

If you'd like to take self-talk to the next level, you can find a complete list of self-talk programs that are certified by the Self-Talk Institute at selftalkplus.com.

November 25

"When I'm working at improving myself in any way, especially when I'm adjusting my weight or getting in shape, I not only practice getting fit, I also practice *patience*. No matter what it takes, or how long it takes, I stay with it and I win."

November 26

"In my old programs I see my own resistance to making changes in my life, my own unnecessary fears about my ability to be fit, weigh the weight I want, and be healthy. They are all old and unnecessary programs, and I choose to get rid of them. I no longer need them, and I will do much better without them."

November 27

"I know that the most important words I ever say, are the words I say to myself. So I make sure I give myself the right dreams, the right goals, the right direction, the right attitude, the right strength, and the thankfulness for what I achieve."

November 28

"I know that every thought I think, or message I get, can physically rewire my brain. So I never let anyone—without my approval—rewire my brain for me. That would include friends, family, work associates, television, social media, or any source of the messages I get. My programs are my choice, not theirs."

November 29

"If I ever think about quitting, or giving up on my health and fitness goals, I take time to get my thinking right. I remember my goal, I regain my focus, I choose to make things work, and I come back stronger than ever."

November 30

"I know that people who smile more, live more. When the smile on my face comes from within, knowing I'm working with purpose, having good goals, living each day in a positive way, and being thankful for the chance to be here, I'm creating the smile that helps my life work right."

Self-Talk Tip #55

Your Brain Can *"Delete"* Old Mental Programs You No Longer Want!

Does your brain, like a computer, have a delete button? In a way, it does. Researchers have learned that in your brain, when you stop using an old program, you stop sending nutrition to that program's neural networks; you stop *feeding* it, and in time your brain will delete it.

Neuroscientists call this "pruning." Like the gardener who cuts out, or prunes, old rose branches to make way for new growth and more beautiful roses, the brain will get rid of pathways you're no longer using to make way for new pathways to form.

If you'd like to prune out old programs you no longer want, the best way we've found to deal with them is to replace them with new programs—new self-talk—which, with enough repetition, will eventually become the stronger programs and take over. When you stop using the old programs, they will lose their nutrition, and in time, your brain will prune them out. And beautiful new roses will grow.

December 1

"Why would I put off a better future when I can start right now? Today I choose to take control of my life, decide what I want to do next, set my goals, put myself into action, and take a clear, strong step forward, into my own incredible, unlimited, positive future."

December 2

"I have learned to see myself in a slim, healthy, attractive way. That's what I see, and that's what I create."

December 3

"How do I make life work best? I choose my self-talk, look for the good, help others, avoid negative habits, avoid negative people, smile a lot, think in a positive and practical way, and work every day to create a life of health, and success."

December 4

"When a challenging or difficult day comes to an end, I let it go. Instead of dwelling on the problems of the day, I focus on what I have learned, and my choice to have a better day tomorrow."

December 5

"I am mindful. Throughout each day I am consciously *aware of being aware*—of my attitude, my actions, my thoughts, and my words. Because I am mindful, I control the direction of my mind and the direction of my day".

December 6

"When it comes to being completely in control of my weight and fitness, the most important thing I can do is to believe in myself. I can set goals, be strong, and work hard, but I also make the choice to believe I can do it."

Self-Talk Tip #56

The Amazing Power
of *Mindfulness*

Being 'mindful' is the art of *being aware of being aware.* There's a good reason for getting good at it. We're not aware of what goes on in most of our brain. Over 90% of our choices are made without our being aware of why we're making them. Most of the brain is working entirely on its own—without our conscious input. (That's where most of our problems come from; unconscious programs are in control of most of what we think and do—and most of our unconscious programs are negative.)

When you consciously practice being mindful, you become aware of what you're thinking, and why, and you take back control of your life from the 90% part of your brain that doesn't tell you what's going on. If you really want to be in control, you have to make being mindful the default, and you have to get good at it. Fortunately, with some practice, you can do that.

Since you're reading this book, it won't surprise you to know that one of the best ways to become mindful of what's going on in your brain is to practice using positive self-talk. When you practice talking to yourself in the most positive, self-directing way each day, you become more mindful of *everything* you're thinking. And being *mindful* is where a successful day begins.

December 7

"Of all the things I have, of all the things that are important to me, the one thing I can always count on is me—my heart, my mind, my faith, and my absolute determination to live my life in a positive way."

December 8

"I know that the real first step to weight control is believing in myself, taking control of my life, and seeing myself the way I really want to be."

December 9

"I like: reaching goals, being organized, staying productive, keeping fit, looking forward, learning new things, feeling great, staying positive, smiling a lot, doing my best, helping others, and always getting better. And every one of those things is up to me."

December 10

"The moment I begin to doubt, I think about the best outcome. The moment I fear, I feel the real strength I have within me. And the moment I think I'm not enough, I remember that I am not alone. With my faith and my undying belief, I am greater than anything that could come against me."

December 11

"More and more each day. I am actually becoming the fit, trim, successful new picture of me that I see in my mind. I see it, I create it, and I become it."

December 12

"I choose to be successful in some way every day. I see mistakes as learning, problems as opportunities, setbacks as starting points, and limitations as a chance to grow. Every new day is an open doorway to my unlimited future, and one more day to practice becoming the incredible me I was intended to be."

Self-Talk Tip #57

Can *Anyone* Make Positive
Self-Talk Work?

Can anyone practice self-talk and make it work for them? The short answer is yes, anyone can do it; *we're all using self-talk all of the time*—it's just that we're not always using the right kind.

The problem is, using bad self-talk is a habit, and one that most people aren't aware of when they're doing it. And because they don't know they're doing it, they also don't know the harm it's doing them. Day after day, negative thought after negative thought, they're wiring negative attitudes and opinions into their brains. In time, the old adage becomes true: they become most what they think about most.

It's precisely the fact that we use self-talk without thinking about it or knowing that we're doing it, that proves anyone can do it. We're all self-talking already.

Practicing positive self-talk is doing what we've been doing all along, but this time changing the words——and getting it right. Doing that is a habit that can be learned. Once you know about positive self-talk, and how it works, you can practice it for yourself. And *anyone* can do it.

December 13

"I never allow negative people to darken my day. They have their life, I have mine. So I refuse to let anyone's negativity affect my day in any way. When I hear someone's *'negative,'* I automatically and immediately replace it with my own healthy, *'positive.'* I think right. I think positive. And because I do, my day works."

December 14

"I know that I have a limited number of hours and minutes to live up to my healthy best each day. So today I choose to use my time in the best possible way. I plan it, I do it, I stay with it, I reach my goals, and I make today count."

December 15

"I improve my fitness by the thoughts I think. My day begins with positive thoughts about my weight-loss goal, and I choose healthy thoughts throughout the day. Every day is filled with the positive, healthy thoughts that improve my life, and every one of them is mine to choose."

December 16

"I live each day with the absolute determination to live that day in the very best way. And when I go to sleep each night, I look forward with positive enthusiasm to a brand new day tomorrow."

December 17

"I begin each day by concentrating and focusing on becoming my new self. I see a picture of me as I intend to be. I see it, I feel it, I believe it, and I create it."

December 18

"If I had just one day to do what I need to do, I would not stop, I would not wait, I would not fear, and I would not give up or give in. That is the way I see today. I know what I need to do, and I do it."

Self-Talk Tip #58
The 'Attitude Diet'

Imagine having a wellness program in which you ate only the right thing, always loved what you ate but never ate too much, looked forward to activity and exercise, always stayed motivated, and never worried about slipping. That may only happen in a perfect world, but there is something that comes close.

Everything you think, believe, or feel about your weight, or diet, or exercise plan starts with the 'attitude' you have *stored* in your mind. Your attitude is 'wired in,' in physical neural networks in your brain. And because the way your attitude is wired determines how you feel about every step of your diet or fitness program, if you really want to create success, *attitude rules.*

This means that successfully losing weight, keeping it off, or getting in shape, all start and end with attitude. And attitude is one thing you can create, change, and control. Your brain is designed to help you do that.

The positive self-talk you read here every day is designed to create the 'attitude diet.' It gives you the words and the programs, which, when wired into place, give you a whole new way to look at being healthy. When your attitude is healthy, the rest of your life—including your weight—will follow your attitude.

December 19

"There has never been a better day than today to work for what I want to achieve. There has never been a better time than right now to take action. And there has never been a better moment than this one to let myself know I can do it."

December 20

"Who says I was born with purpose and potential? Who says I can be the incredible person I was meant to be? Who says I can reach any goal I set for myself? Who says I can be the winner I choose to be? Who says all that, and who believes it about me? I do!"

December 21

"I choose to create 'quiet time' in my life. Time for my thoughts, time for my dreams, time to be thankful, and time to create the amazing life I choose to live tomorrow. When I take time for myself, I'm not 'borrowing time' from something else—I'm creating the incredible future I have in front of me!"

December 22

"I choose to be determined, strong, resolute, and unstoppable. I have courage, strength, and conviction. I was born to succeed, and that's exactly what I choose to do. I have what it takes to make my life work, and right now is a great time to prove it."

December 23

"I know that the only thing holding me back from living up to my true potential, is nothing more than fear. Fear of failure, fear of change, fear of what other people think, fear of the unknown, fear of inadequacy, fear of rejection, or any other fear I have. And I also know that all these fears are false."

December 24

"I have made the decision to make an important and positive change in my life. I have chosen to take care of myself in every healthy way, today and every day."

Self-Talk Tip #59

How to Make Any Day a Better Day

The next time you have a bad day, or when it seems like nothing is going right, there is something you can do that will help. Your *attitude* about what's happening, how you feel about anything, is never up to what's happening around you. What *tells* you how you feel about what's happening, is up to you and the attitude you *choose*.

So on the next 'bad day' try this: Give yourself positive self-talk that lets you know (1) You're okay, (2) You can get through this, (3) Life, overall, is going to go on—it usually does—and (4) Your attitude is up to you.

When the day looks bad, and some old negative programs are working against you, read a page or two of the self-talk in this book. If you listen to recorded self-talk, choose one of your favorite sessions and listen to it. When you do this, you'll actually be adjusting important chemicals in your brain. The more you read or listen to the right self-talk, the better your attitude will get, and life will once again become worthwhile, and not 'that bad.' And it can happen in just minutes.

When you switch to positive self-talk, not only will you look at things in a more positive light, but you could also feel even better than you did before the problem came up.

December 25

"I'm never afraid to dream. I believe in the best for my future; I dream it, I see it, I prepare for it, I work at it, I create it, and I make it happen. I choose to live up to the best of my dreams, and I choose to make my dreams come true."

December 26

"Each day I renew my goal to live right, eat right, and reach my important personal goal of being super fit in every way."

December 27

"My goal is to become the individual I have always dreamed of being. And that includes maintaining the right, healthy weight for me."

December 28

"I look for ways to improve myself every chance I get. And because I listen, learn, search, study, practice and apply, I always build, improve, achieve, excel, overcome, and win."

December 29

"I have faith. My spirit, my belief, and my personal strength are alive and well within me. So I move ahead, believing in the most positive possible outcome, and bravely take the next step forward into my incredible future. I have faith, and I am not afraid to live up to my highest calling."

December 30

"Who am I? I am the very best of the person I choose to be. What do I want? To reach every goal I set, in the most healthy and positive way. Where am I going? Into a future that is filled with the promise of my own possibilities. How do I know? Because that's who I choose to be."

December 31

"Each day I look at myself in the mirror, smile, nod my head 'Yes!,' and tell myself the self-talk that says, *'I choose to make today an incredible day in every way!'* And then, in everything I think and everything I do, I create it, I live it, and I make it happen."

You are invited to join Self-Talk+Plus™

If you would like to join an online community of positive self-talkers—people like you who are working to make their lives better—you are invited to join Self-Talk+Plus™. This is the inspiring online community where members stream self-talk to their smartphones, get to know each other, join in online activities, receive help from experienced life coaches, and share ideas that help them reach their goals. To visit this amazing online community go to **selftalkplus.com**.

 Listen to Certified Self-Talk Programs™ on your tablet or smartphone today at selftalkplus.com.

Printed in Great Britain
by Amazon